Ph-95

C000178600

EXPERIMENTAL MEASUREMENTS:
PRECISION, ERROR AND TRUTH

EXPERIMENTAL MEASUREMENTS: PRECISION, ERROR AND TRUTH

Second Edition

N. C. BARFORD
Imperial College, London

JOHN WILEY & SONS
Chichester – New York – Brisbane – Toronto – Singapore

SCHLUMBERGER
ELECTRONICS (UK) LTD.
No.
11289
LIBRARY

Copyright © 1967 by Addison-Wesley Publishing Company, Inc. (1st edn.)

Copyright © 1985 by John Wiley & Sons Ltd. (2nd edn.)

All rights reserved.

No part of this book may be reproduced by any means, nor transmitted, nor translated into a machine language without the written permission of the publisher

Library of Congress Cataloging in Publication Data:

Barford, N. C.
  Experimental measurements.

  Bibliography: p.
  Includes index.
  1. Errors, Theory of. 2.   Physical measurements.
I. Title.
QA275.B27   1985   511′.43   84-29930
ISBN 0 471 90701 4 (cloth)
ISBN 0 471 90702 2 (paper)

British Library Cataloguing in Publication Data:

Barford, N. C.
  Experimental measurements: precision, error and
  truth.—2nd ed.
  1. Mensuration   2. Errors, Theory of
  I. Title
  530.8′01′5195   T50

ISBN 0 471 90701 4 (cloth)
ISBN 0 471 90702 2 (paper)

Printed and Bound in Great Britain

To Janet

Preface

Words like error, accurate, truth, probable, likelihood, are part of everyday language. For most of us their meanings may not be mathematically precise, but the ideas behind them reflect experience we have gained from an early age.

One way of approaching the subject matter of this book is to step aside from this experience and to talk of tossing coins and rolling dice, of the laws of probability that these activities demonstrate and the statistical predictions that may be derived from them. This is undoubtedly the concise method. Terms may be introduced as precise definitions, a clear and elegant mathematical structure constructed and, finally, the measurements of actual experiments analysed from the viewpoint of this theory.

However, work goes on in school and college laboratory and measurements pile up while theory is established and learnt. I think that for many students the better approach is one that sharpens the ideas they already have by asking questions about the interpretation of actual experiments right from the beginning. By obtaining quantitative answers that accord with qualitative notions already held one can very quickly gain a viewpoint from which a systematic appraisal is possible—one that needs nothing more than elementary mathematics for description and least squares as a connecting principle. The first three chapters are devoted to such an approach and could be used even by sixth-form pupils as a working guide to the treatment of experimental measurements.

This approach gives precision to the common sense answers to many questions, but poses others which call for a theory of errors—that is, a model which will produce errors and statistical fluctuations that can be tested against experiment. This is developed in Chapters 4 and 5, in which the Gaussian and Poisson distributions are derived and discussed. In the final chapter topics such as maximum likelihood and the testing of hypotheses are used to illustrate the much greater field of interest and understanding that the theory opens up.

Cross-references are given to further comments on points of importance and to the worked examples illustrating them. These are collected at the end of each chapter, rather than dispersed throughout the text, so that the main line of development is not interrupted. For very few of us is the theory of errors an end in itself. For this reason many of the worked and unworked examples are exercises in experimental judgment, rather than mere tests of arithmetical skills. As an aid to easy reference a summary of the principal results is given on pages 139 to 146.

I should like to thank Professor A. J. Forty and Mr. J. H. Pain for their helpful comments and Mrs. S. Hulbert for computing the tables of the appendices. I am especially grateful to Dr. P. R. Doidge and Dr. K. H. Ruddock who read the manuscript with such care and suggested many improvements.

Imperial College   N.C.B.
February 1967

Preface to the Second Edition

A new edition is a temptation to turn what starts as a 'working book', for everyday use and ready reference in the laboratory, into a near treatise that includes all the topics and discussion that earlier readers had wished it to include. I have resisted this temptation and hope that the modest amount of material I have added will not change its character.

Some consists of slightly expanded comments, and of laying more emphasis, on particular points where confusion recurs in every new year of students, for example over the fundamental importance of distinguishing clearly between the standard deviation of individual measurements and the standard deviation of their mean. The main addition, however, comes from carrying further the discussion of the 'best straight line' to encompass the more general topic of linear regression and the coefficient of regression.

The derivation of the Gaussian distribution is now a little tidier and I trust that the slips and errors that evaded detection in the first edition have been corrected, without adding new ones, in this.

Imperial College,   N.C.B.
March 1985

Contents

CHAPTER 1

Introduction

Measurement is fundamental to the growth and application of science. From the cutting of stone blocks to build pyramids and the timing of eclipses to inaugurate religious ceremonies to the counting of blood cells and the determination of the shape of the earth from satellite orbits, the methods and techniques of measurement have been extended and improved and our dependence on their reliability has increased.

But making a measurement is not enough. When we come to use the result we want to know if it is good enough for our purposes. Is the elastic modulus for an aluminium alloy quoted in a reference book a safe basis for designing an aircraft wing? Does a measurement of the amount of energy from radio stars support or disprove the steady state theory of the universe? The purpose of this short book is to show how the results of experiments and their reliability can be presented and assessed in an objective way. The ideas and arguments will develop from considering a typical case that might occur in a school or college laboratory.

1.1 JENKINS VERSUS ROBINSON

Two students were asked to time the oscillations of the same pendulum. Jenkins said the period was 1.4 sec; Robinson said it was 1.53 sec. Which was to be believed—Jenkins because he seemed a dependable sort of person, or Robinson because he gave the result to two decimal places?

A golden rule in experimental physics is to make sure how much information really comes from the experimental results, and how much from preconceptions about the experiment or the person carrying it out. What we have to decide here is not only the period of the pendulum, but the reliability of the measurements made. A single numerical result from an experiment cannot, by itself, give both pieces of information. At least two numbers are required if an experiment is to give a result and a measure of its

[See §1.5.2,
page 19]

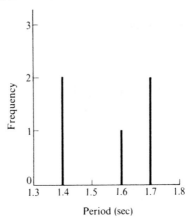

Period (sec)   **Figure 1.1**

reliability, although, as we shall see later, it is much more useful to
include yet a third.

[See §1.5.1,
page 18]
Of course, if we can have only one result from each experiment
and we need to use the period in a theoretical formula or the
design of some other apparatus, we shall have to fall back on the
impression Jenkins made or on Robinson's second decimal point,
although it could be that Jenkins was simply an accomplished actor
and Robinson put in the last figure at random to create a good
impression.

It is far more satisfactory to ask Jenkins and Robinson to
repeat their measurements. The first five results from Jenkins were
1.4, 1.7, 1.4, 1.6 and 1.7 sec and those from Robinson were 1.53,
1.50, 1.51, 1.52 and 1.51 sec. We can compare these results best
by plotting them as *frequency distributions*, with measurement
value as abscissa and the number of times each value is found as
ordinate (figures 1.1 and 1.2).

This gives a very different view of the matter. For one thing,
both experimenters revised their original estimates. Each decided
to give the *arithmetic average* or *mean* of his results, so that
Jenkins then said the period was $(1.4 + 1.7 + 1.4 + 1.6 + 1.7)/5 =$
[See §1.5.3,
page 19]
1.56 sec instead of 1.4 sec while Robinson said it was $(1.53 +
1.50 + 1.51 + 1.52 + 1.51)/5 = 1.514$ sec instead of 1.53 sec. Sec-
ondly, we have an objective way of comparing the two experiments. Robinson's measurements are closely bunched together,
none less than 1.50 sec or greater than 1.53 sec, while Jenkins'
spread from 1.4 sec to 1.7 sec. Robinson's look more accurate than
Jenkins' and, although we cannot be very precise about what we

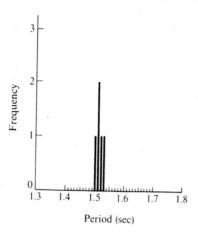

Figure 1.2

mean by 'more accurate', these two distributions are sufficiently different for Robinson's value of 1.514 sec to be preferred to Jenkins' 1.56 sec.

However, Jenkins was not prepared to take this lying down. He put several hours' work in and came back with 500 measurements and a mean value of 1.5326 sec. His frequency distribution is now as given in figure 1.3.

This is still a much broader one than Robinson's and in this sense is inferior. But should not some credit be given to the fact that it represents 500 measurements instead of just the 5 that Robinson made?

Whom should we believe at this stage—Jenkins or Robinson? And what is the correct value for the period? In what follows we

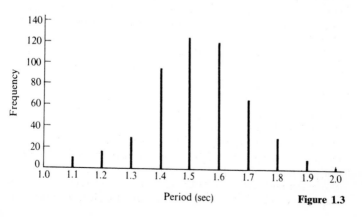

Figure 1.3

shall try to show how a systematic way of analysing experimental results will help us to answer these questions. We shall see that there is no one 'correct' answer to any problem of this type. However, there are usually good grounds on which we can agree about the 'best' answer, and even if this agreement cannot be reached, a clear method of looking at the problem will at least enable us to see just what we are disagreeing about.

1.2   THE INFINITE EXPERIMENT

A fundamental question that arose from the discussion of the previous section was how to express the importance of repeating measurements. Most of us would agree that it is important—we would attach a greater value to Jenkins' 500 measurements than to his 5. But we should like to find some *numerical* way of expressing this that would enable us to compare his 500 with the 5 of Robinson. Just what is it that changes as the number of measurements increases? What would happen if we increased this number indefinitely—if we carried out an *infinite* experiment?

Since the results of any number of measurements can be represented as a frequency distribution, we can follow an experiment through by plotting this distribution as more and more measurements are made. Figures 1.1 and 1.3 show it at the 5-measurement and 500-measurement stage for Jenkins' experiment. It is, then, changes in this distribution that we must try to relate to the number of measurements made.

1.2.1   Relative frequency distribution: normalization

One obvious way in which the distribution changes is that the ordinates become larger and larger as the total number of measurements increases. It is difficult to compare the results of 5 measurements with those of 500 if we use the same scale. It is better to present the results as *relative frequency distributions*, where the ordinates are not the actual or absolute number of times a measurement is recorded but the ratio of this number to the total number of measurements made at that stage. The results of figures 1.1 and 1.3 in relative frequency distribution form would then be as shown in figures 1.4 and 1.5.

From now on we shall nearly always use frequency to mean *relative* frequency rather than *absolute* frequency. It is easy to see which is meant, for relative frequency is always a fraction of the whole and the ordinates of the distribution will be less than 1 (for example, figures 1.4 and 1.5). Absolute frequencies count the

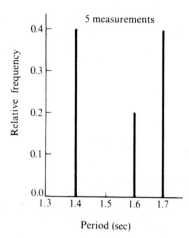

Figure 1.4

actual number of times each measurement is made, so that each ordinate, if it is not zero, will have a value of at least 1 (for example, figures 1.1, 1.2 and 1.3).

It is essential, when presenting results as a relative frequency distribution, to record with it the total number of measurements made. As we shall see later, both the distribution and this number are required for the proper interpretation of an experiment.

Suppose that, when a total of n measurements of a quantity x have been made, an experiment shows that x_1 was recorded n_1 times, x_2 was recorded n_2 times, $\ldots$, x_m, n_m times. Now

$$n = n_1 + n_2 + \ldots + n_m,$$
(1.1)

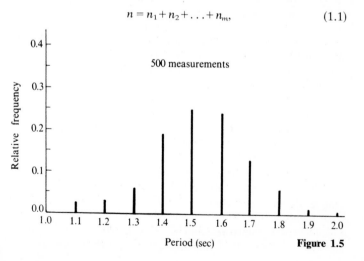

Figure 1.5

so that the ordinates of the relative frequency distribution at the values $x_1, x_2, \ldots, x_m$ will be

$$f_n(x_1) = n_1/n, \qquad f_n(x_2) = n_2/n, \quad \ldots, \quad f_n(x_m) = n_m/n. \quad (1.2)$$

Then

$$f_n(x_1) + f_n(x_2) + \ldots + f_n(x_m) = (n_1 + n_2 + \ldots + n_m)/n = 1. \quad (1.3)$$

A distribution with this property is said to be *normalized*, so that changing a frequency distribution from absolute to relative form is equivalent to *normalizing* the distribution.

See §1.5.4, page 19]

1.2.2 Limiting frequency distribution

Figures 1.4 and 1.5 show that even when they are normalized, frequency distributions fluctuate as the total number of measurements increases. It is an experimental fact that for most experiments these fluctuations are quite large and erratic for small numbers of measurements. We find, for example, that the distribution for 5 measurements will usually look rather different from that for 10. However, as the numbers increase the fluctuations decrease. There are differences, but much less marked, between the distributions for 50 and 100 measurements, and when we come to compare 500 and 1000 measurements the difference between their normalized frequency distributions will be negligible.

We usually have no way of predicting exactly what the fluctuations will be, only that the distribution settles down to a more and more definite shape as the number of measurements increases. This we summarize by saying that there is a *limiting frequency distribution* for the *infinite experiment*. This limiting distribution is the basis of the whole of our subsequent discussion. We shall denote it without a subscript, so that $f(x_1), f(x_2), \ldots, f(x_m)$ are the relative frequencies of recording the measurements $x_1, x_2, \ldots, x_m$ in the infinite experiment (see figure 1.6).

It is very important to realize that the existence of this limiting distribution is nearly always an assumption. We can never really test it satisfactorily. If an experimentalist keeps on and on making a measurement he may become tired and careless, or the apparatus will begin to wear out, both of which will tend to broaden the frequency distribution. Or it may be that the quantity that is being measured is itself varying with time—room temperature, for example—so that the frequency distribution will drift up or down as the measurements are repeated. The assumption implies that with sufficient ingenuity we could make the measurements as many times as we like *without any change* in the properties of the

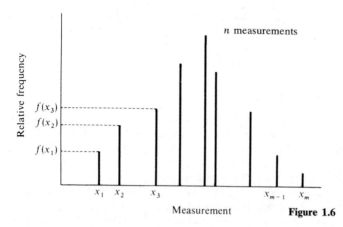

n measurements

Figure 1.6

apparatus, the observer, or the quantity that is being observed—a matter which clearly cannot be put to the test.

So our whole analysis of experimental errors is built upon an assumption, and this may seem to be a very uncertain and unsatisfactory basis for an important part of science. However, we should not feel furtive about this. All scientific theories start from some assumptions, although they are often not clearly stated or understood. There is an honourable and well-tested way of proceeding in these circumstances. We simply develop the theory to the extent that it makes predictions that can be tested against experimental results or other theories. If discrepancies appear we look back along our line of argument, examining each assumption as we come to it, to see how necessary it was to enable us to develop the theory and to see what possible changes could remove the discrepancy.

It is safe to say that any experiment occurring in a school or undergraduate course is extremely unlikely to cast doubt on our initial assumption of a limiting frequency distribution and that it should be possible to resolve the discrepancies that do occur on a less deep and philosophical plane than the revision of this basic assumption.

1.2.3 Discrete value distribution

In talking about frequency distributions we have implied that any one of a number of quite precise measurements $x_1, x_2, \ldots, x_m$ may be recorded. For some types of experiments this is true enough. If x is the number of days in which rain falls during a year, x could have any integer value from 0 to 366.

For such an experiment a *discrete value distribution* of the sort we have shown in figures 1.1 to 1.6 is appropriate. We may note that the measurements $x_1, x_2, \ldots, x_m$ need not be finite in number, nor need they be equally spaced. The properties 1.1, 1.2 and 1.3 are, of course, always true.

1.2.4 Histogram

Quite often discrete values are inappropriate. If we were measuring a group of children each year to see how they were growing, there would be no set of exact heights that could describe every child. Growth is a gradual or continuous process, so that even if we set up apparatus that would measure in intervals of 0.1 mm, this would not imply that children grew by suddenly lengthening in steps of 0.1 mm from time to time. In practice such precision would be of little value, and it would probably be sufficient to divide heights into 1 cm intervals, and find what proportion of the children had heights within each of these.

More generally, if x is a continuous variable, that is one which *could* have any value (perhaps only within some restricted range), we decide on intervals with endpoints $x_0, x_1, x_2, \ldots, x_m$ and determine from an experiment the relative frequencies of measurements lying within them:

$$n_1/n \quad \text{with} \quad x_0 \le x \le x_1,$$
$$n_2/n \quad \text{with} \quad x_1 < x \le x_2,$$
$$\vdots \qquad \qquad \vdots$$
$$n_m/n \quad \text{with} \quad x_{m-1} < x \le x_m,$$

where $n = n_1 + n_2 + \ldots + n_m$ is the total number of measurements. These values are shown as rectangles based on each measurement interval, each of area equal to the relative frequency for that interval. Together they constitute a *normalized histogram* of the results (figure 1.7).

The heights of the rectangles, $f_n(x_1), f_n(x_2), \ldots, f_n(x_m)$, are the ordinates of the histogram and are such that:

$(x_1 - x_0)f_n(x_1)$ is the (relative) frequency
$\quad = n_1/n \quad$ of obtaining a measurement $x_0 \le x \le x_1$,

$(x_2 - x_1)f_n(x_2)$ is the (relative) frequency
$\quad = n_2/n \quad$ of obtaining a measurement $x_1 < x \le x_2$,

$$\vdots \qquad \qquad \vdots$$

$(x_m - x_{m-1})f_n(x_m)$ is the (relative) frequency
$\quad = n_m/n \quad$ of obtaining a measurement $x_{m-1} < x \le x_m$.

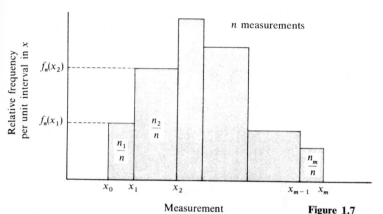

Figure 1.7

$$\text{Area under histogram} = (x_1 - x_0)f_n(x_1) + (x_2 - x_1)f_n(x_2) + \ldots$$
$$+ (x_m - x_{m-1})f_n(x_m)$$
$$= (n_1 + n_2 + \ldots + n_m)/n$$
$$= 1, \tag{1.4}$$

which expresses the certainty of obtaining some value of x from a normalized histogram.

Note that the intervals $x_1 - x_0, x_2 - x_1, \ldots, x_m - x_{m-1}$ do not need to be equal and that $f_n(x_1), f_n(x_2), \ldots, f_n(x_m)$ are adjusted in inverse ratio to the lengths of the respective intervals to take account of this. In other words, $f_n(x)$ is the relative frequency *per unit interval in x*—to obtain the actual relative frequency we must multiply this by the appropriate interval.

The results of all experiments that involve the measurement of only one quantity can be represented by one or other of the two types of chart discussed in sections 1.2.3 and 1.2.4. Either measurements are intrinsically discrete (as in the rainy day experiment), or the nature of the apparatus or the use to which we put the results requires them to be grouped within intervals of a continuous variable. [See §1.5.5 page 21; §1.5.6, page 22]

1.2.5 Continuous distribution

We can deal with both the preceding cases together if we imagine a smooth curve to be drawn through the outline of the charts (figures 1.8 and 1.9). If we label the curve $F_n(x)$, then when it is used to represent a discrete value distribution it has the property [See §1.5.7 page 22]

$$F_n(x_1) = f_n(x_1), \qquad F_n(x_2) = f_n(x_2), \qquad \ldots, \qquad F_n(x_m) = f_n(x_m).$$

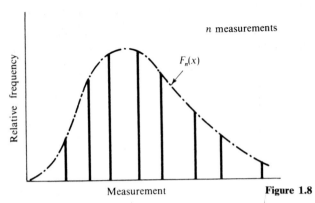

Figure 1.8

When it is used to represent a histogram, $F_n(x)$ is approximately equal to the height of each rectangle at the midpoint of the interval. More precisely, it is chosen so that the area under each section is equal to the corresponding area under the histogram,

$$\int_{x_{r-1}}^{x_r} F_n(x)\,dx = (x_r - x_{r-1})f_n(x_r),$$

Hence

$$\int_{-\infty}^{\infty} F_n(x)\,dx = (x_1 - x_0)f_n(x_1) + (x_2 - x_1)f_n(x_2) + \ldots$$
$$+ (x_m - x_{m-1})f_n(x_m) = 1. \tag{1.5}$$

We shall, from now on, nearly always think in terms of continuous frequency distribution curves, although it should be remembered that they are really only convenient approximations.

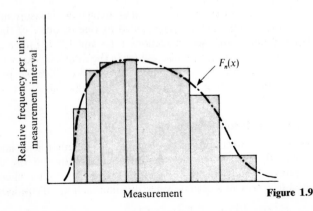

Figure 1.9

1.3   TRUE VALUE: MEAN, MODE AND MEDIAN

The limiting frequency distribution curve represents in a compact form all the information that an experiment can yield. Both the physical quantity that is being measured and the apparatus (counting the experimentalist or observer as part of the 'apparatus') are somehow involved in determining the position and shape of the curve. We must try to separate the effects of these two.

Sometimes the curve is determined entirely by the quantity that is being measured—it represents an intrinsic feature of that quantity. Suppose, for example, we examined a large number of grasshoppers to see how many legs they had. Nearly always we should count six. Sometimes we should count five or fewer if the grasshopper had met with an accident, or there might be some genetic defect which could give rise to fewer or possibly even more than six. If we counted the legs of more and more grasshoppers the frequency distribution would settle down and approach its limiting form. It would be something like that shown in figure 1.10.

The physical quantity we are observing is the number of legs and this determines the distribution entirely. The 'apparatus' is the observer with his pencil and paper for recording the results, and has no effect upon the distribution.

It is true that the apparatus *could* affect the result. The observer's eyes might be weak so that he sometimes fails to see a leg that is there, and sometimes imagines one that does not exist. Or, even if he counts correctly, he may write down the result incorrectly. But if we discount this, which is equivalent to saying

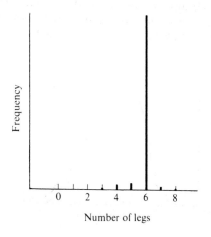

Number of legs

Figure 1.10

that the apparatus is quite precise or accurate, the form of the distribution tells us that:

1. A grasshopper can have any number of legs from 0 to 8.

2. The overwhelming majority have 6 legs—we might call this the normal or natural number.

3. Accidents or abnormalities are much more likely to give fewer than 6 legs than to give more.

In this case what we are measuring is a rather complex matter. There is one number, 6, that comes clearly out of the results, but this one number is insufficient to describe fully either the limiting frequency distribution or the particular characteristics of the grasshoppers from which it is derived. A result that needs more than one number to describe it gives rise, naturally, to a distribution that needs more than one number to describe it.

However, there are many quantities that we believe can be described by a single number—the mass of a metal block, the period of a pendulum, the charge of an electron, for example. But even in these cases, as we have seen in the Jenkins and Robinson experiments, there will be a frequency distribution curve.

See §1.5.8, page 22]

Now such a curve cannot be described by the single number that we are attempting to measure. No one number alone can describe the position *and* shape of anything. So what are we to make of a limiting curve like the one in Figure 1.11? In what way does the single number quantity affect the curve?

It is better to invert this question and ask instead what we would indeed ask of the experiment—given the curve, what is the value of the quantity we are trying to measure? This can be answered most easily when the limiting frequency distribution curve is symmetrical, with a single peak (figures 1.12 and 1.13).

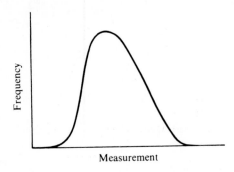

Figure 1.11

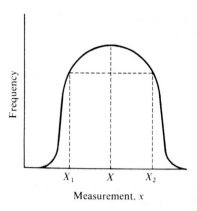

Measurement, x   **Figure 1.12**

The true value is then the value at the central axis of symmetry of the curve, X. The most powerful argument for this is that it could not very well be any other value. For example, if X_1 were chosen in figure 1.12 or 1.13 it is difficult to see how any argument for this choice, *based solely on the evidence of the frequency curve*, could not equally well be used for X_2, the symmetrically opposed value.

Only X has unique properties. Among them are the following:

1. It is the *mean* of all the measurements.

2. It is the *mode*—the value with the greatest frequency.

3. It is the *median*—measurements above and below X occur equally frequently, so that the ordinate through X divides the area under the curve into two equal parts.

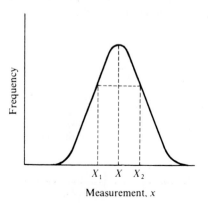

Measurement, x   **Figure 1.13**

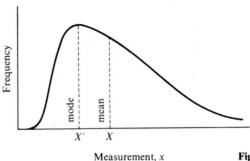

Measurement, x   **Figure 1.14**

Any of these properties could be used to *define* what we mean by the true value, and in this case they all give the same value. If the curve is not symmetrical we shall usually obtain different values. For example, for the curve shown in figure 1.14 it is clear that the mean value, X, is different from the mode, X'. In such cases it is a matter of convention which is chosen as the true value. Occasionally there may be good reasons for preferring one of the alternatives, but if not we shall always take as the true value the *arithmetic mean derived from the limiting frequency distribution*.

The mean is calculated as follows:

1. *Discrete value distribution.* Multiply each measurement value by the relative frequency with which it occurs and sum over all possible values,

$$X = \bar{x} = x_1 f(x_1) + x_2 f(x_2) + \ldots + x_m f(x_m). \tag{1.6}$$

2. *Histogram.* Multiply the mid-value of the measurement in each interval by the relative frequency for that interval and sum over all possible values,

$$X = \bar{x} = \tfrac{1}{2}(x_1 + x_0)(x_1 - x_0)f(x_1) + \tfrac{1}{2}(x_2 + x_1)(x_2 - x_1)f(x_2) + \ldots$$
$$+ \tfrac{1}{2}(x_m + x_{m-1})(x_m - x_{m-1})f(x_m). \tag{1.7}$$

3. *Distribution curve.* Multiply the measurement value by the corresponding distribution curve function and integrate over all values—that is, the smooth curve approximation to the preceeding expression,

$$X = \bar{x} = \int_{-\infty}^{\infty} xF(x)\, dx. \tag{1.8}$$

1.4 PRECISION OF THE APPARATUS: STANDARD DEVIATION

Suppose the same single number physical quantity is measured in two different experiments, involving different apparatus. If both limiting frequency distribution curves are single peaked and symmetrical, they should give the same value for the position of the peak. We should, therefore, expect something like figure 1.15. Note that the narrower curve must have the taller peak since the areas under the two curves must be equal,

$$1 = \int_{-\infty}^{\infty} F_{\mathrm{I}}(x)\ dx = \int_{-\infty}^{\infty} F_{\mathrm{II}}(x)\ dx.$$

What, besides the common value X, determines these curves? Since the only other factor determining them is the apparatus, the shape, as opposed to the position, must reflect in some way the properties of the apparatus. Of these its accuracy or precision is our concern, and although it is extremely difficult to define this in a comprehensive way, most of us would agree that $F_{\mathrm{I}}(x)$ indicates a greater precision than $F_{\mathrm{II}}(x)$. Comparing them, we see that a far greater proportion of the measurements obtained from experiment I (with the narrow distribution) will lie close to the true value, X, than those from experiment II (with the broad distribution). This, roughly, is what we mean by saying that experiment I has a greater precision than experiment II. The problem remains how to measure this precision in some simple, systematic, numerical way—that is, if possible, by another single number that determines the 'width' of the curve.

Any particular measurement x will differ from the true value X

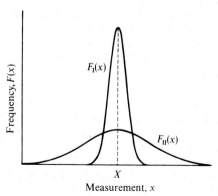

Measurement, x **Figure 1.15**

by an error, or deviation from the true value,

$$\varepsilon = x - X.$$

Large errors clearly correspond to broadly peaked curves, so some measure of their average size will give us the sort of number we are looking for.

The average error will not do, for this is necessarily zero:

$$\int_{-\infty}^{\infty} \varepsilon F(x)\, dx = \int_{-\infty}^{\infty} (x - X)F(x)\, dx$$

$$= \int_{-\infty}^{\infty} xF(x)\, dx - X\int_{-\infty}^{\infty} F(x)\, dx$$

$$= X - X = 0.$$

There are many ways of obtaining a measure of the average *magnitude* of the errors—the two simplest are as follows:

1. *The mean absolute deviation,*

$$\tau = \int_{-\infty}^{\infty} |\varepsilon|\, F(x)\, dx = \int_{-\infty}^{\infty} |x - X|\, F(x)\, dx.$$

2. *The mean square deviation, or variance,*

$$\sigma^2 = \int_{-\infty}^{\infty} \varepsilon^2 F(x)\, dx = \int_{-\infty}^{\infty} (x - X)^2 F(x)\, dx.$$

The *root mean square deviation*, σ, is then called the *standard deviation*. In the first case we take the absolute value of the error, multiply it by the relative frequency with which x is observed, and sum over all values. In the second case we use the squares of the errors instead of their absolute values. Either way we obtain a positive quantity which is larger, the broader the curve, at any rate for those of the type shown in figure 1.15. The smaller either quantity is, the more precision the apparatus has.

Once more, it is a matter of definition which is taken as a true measure of the precision of the apparatus. We shall see later that there is a close link between using the mean as the true value of the quantity being measured and the standard deviation as a measure of precision. We shall therefore adopt the second definition. It must be emphasized, however, that precision is too complex a concept to be completely described in this way. For example, the standard deviations of the symmetric distributions of both figures 1.16 and 1.17 are 0.578. In the first case, however, the

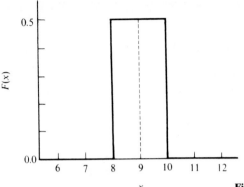

Figure 1.16

experiment would never give a value more than ± 1 from the true value, 9, whereas the second would give 8% of measurements outside these values.

When asymmetrical distributions occur the standard deviation is even less a guide to an assessment of the apparatus. Only the complete curve can really be trusted. Nevertheless, if a single number has to be given, there is usually no better measure of precision of the apparatus than the *standard deviation of the limiting frequency distribution*, σ. This, with caution, we shall adopt as our definition of precision. Since σ^2 is the mean value of ε^2 or

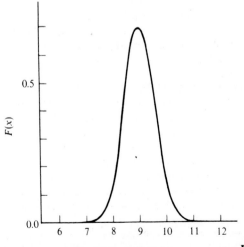

Figure 1.17

$(x - X)^2$, it has, for the discrete distribution, a form similar to Equation 1.6:

$$\sigma^2 = \overline{\varepsilon^2} = (x_1 - X)^2 f(x_1) + (x_2 - X)^2 f(x_2) + \ldots$$
$$+ (x_m - X)^2 f(x_m) \tag{1.9}$$

and, for the histogram, one similar to Equation 1.7:

$$\sigma^2 = \overline{\varepsilon^2} = [\tfrac{1}{2}(x_1 + x_0) - X]^2(x_1 - x_0)f(x_1)$$
$$+ [\tfrac{1}{2}(x_2 + x_1) - X]^2(x_2 - x_1)f(x_2) + \ldots$$
$$+ [\tfrac{1}{2}(x_m + x_{m-1}) - X]^2(x_m - x_{m-1})f(x_m). \tag{1.10}$$

For the continuous distribution, as we have already seen,

$$\sigma^2 = \overline{\varepsilon^2} = \int_{-\infty}^{\infty} (x - X)^2 F(x)\, dx. \tag{1.11}$$

Expanding Equation 1.11,

$$\sigma^2 = \int_{-\infty}^{\infty} x^2 F(x)\, dx - 2X\int_{-\infty}^{\infty} xF(x)\, dx + X^2\int_{-\infty}^{\infty} F(x)\, dx,$$

which, using Equations 1.5 and 1.8, gives

$$\sigma^2 = \int_{-\infty}^{\infty} x^2 F(x)\, dx - X^2.$$

The first term on the right is $\overline{x^2}$, the mean value of x^2. Thus we obtain the useful alternative from,

$$\sigma^2 = \overline{x^2} - X^2 = \overline{x^2} - (\bar{x})^2, \tag{1.12}$$

which is true whatever the form of the distribution.

1.5 COMMENTS AND WORKED EXAMPLES

1.5.1 (See page 2)

We might, for example, wish to test the formula for the period of a simple pendulum,

$$T = 2\pi(l/g)^{\frac{1}{2}}.$$

If Robinson and Jenkins both agreed that the length of the pendulum was 57.25 cm this would give

$$T = 2 \times 3.1416 \times (57.25/981)^{\frac{1}{2}} \text{ sec}$$

$$= 1.518 \text{ sec corrected to three decimal places.}$$

Robinson's single value supports the theory very well while Jenkins' does not. If we are to pass judgment on the theory we have to decide which result we trust. We must particularly beware of accepting Robinson's measurement because it 'agrees with theory'. This is to play the dangerous game of choosing measurements that fit theory—it seems more honourable than actually inventing measurements to fit, but from a scientific point of view they are equally disreputable practices.

If we have good reason to believe Jenkins then the theory is either wrong or inadequately describes the motion of the pendulum under investigation.

1.5.2 (See page 2)

As in any graphical presentation of results the scales and their zeros should be chosen so that the experimental information spreads reasonably well over the space available. Thus in figure 1.1 the horizontal scale extends only from 1.3 to 1.8 sec. If it started at 0 sec we should have all the useful information crammed into a small region at the right.

Figure 1.2 seems to contradict this advice since all the results are here concentrated in a small part of the chart near the value 1.5 sec. However, this is done deliberately in order to emphasize the contrast with figure 1.1.

1.5.3 (See page 2)

Robinson's estimate still apparently supports the simple pendulum theory better than Jenkins's does. However, if we look at the range of values found by the latter it spreads well on either side of the theoretical prediction. We could not say that Jenkins' results considered as a whole contradict the theory.

1.5.4   Example 1 (See page 6)

Repeated measurements of the height of a building gave the following results, corrected to two decimal places: 33.48, 33.46, 33.49, 33.50, 33.49, 33.51, 33.48, 33.50, 33.47, 33.48, 33.49, 33.50, 33.47, 33.51, 33.50, 33.48 m. Present these as a frequency distribution in (a) absolute form, and (b) relative or normalized form.

a) The measurements range from 33.46 to 33.51 m so the horizontal scale could conveniently stretch from, say, 33.45 to

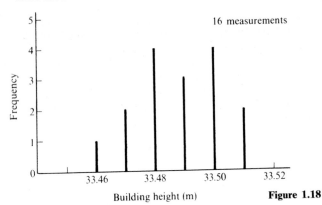

Figure 1.18

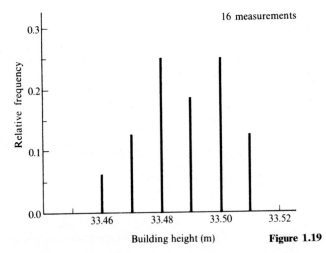

Figure 1.19

33.52 m. The measurements 33.48 and 33.50 occur most frequently (four times) so the vertical scale need rise only to 4. The absolute frequency distribution is therefore as shown in figure 1.18. The total number of measurements (16) can be found by summing all the ordinates. However, it is useful to give this number with the distribution.

b) Since the total number of measurements is 16, the ordinates of the normalized distribution will be those of the absolute distribution, each divided by 16. The greatest will be $\frac{4}{16} = 0.25$, so that the vertical scale need stretch only this far. The horizontal scale will, of course, remain the same. The normalized distribution is then as in figure 1.19. There is no way of telling from a normalized frequency distribution what is the total number of measurements. If we are to present as much information as is given in the original measurements it is therefore essential to give this total with the distribution.

1.5.5 (See page 9)

The measurements of Example 1 are not true discrete values, although they may appear so by being corrected to two decimal places. It is often better to treat such measurements as continuous and then to group them into a histogram presentation, as in the following example.

Example 2

The measurements of Example 1, before correction, were 33.478..., 33.457..., 33.492..., 33.500..., 33.493..., 33.512..., 33.475..., 33.504..., 33.473..., 33.482..., 33.492..., 33.501..., 33.472..., 33.509..., 33.502..., 33.477...m. Present these in normalized histogram form with intervals of 0.01 m.

Suitable end-points for the intervals would be 33.45,

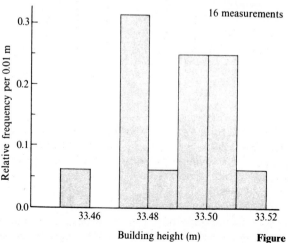

Figure 1.20

33.46, ..., 33.51, 33.52 m. The number of measurements lying within the intervals is respectively 1, 0, 5, 1, 4, 4, 1—total 16—so that the relative frequencies are $\frac{1}{16}$, 0, $\frac{5}{16}$, $\frac{1}{16}$, $\frac{4}{16}$, $\frac{4}{16}$, $\frac{1}{16}$. The histogram is therefore of the form shown in figure 1.20.

1.5.6 (See page 9)

Although it may be best to group measurements of a continuous quantity in histogram form, it is common, at any rate when they are first made, to record the measurements as single numbers rather than to say which interval they fall in. However, no measurement is precise in the sense of yielding an infinite number of significant figures and some convention about the meaning of a measurement expressed as a finite number of figures is necessary. When a group of such measurements is given the interpretation is usually obvious. For example, we should assume that each of 12.32, 12.35, 12.41, 12.39, 12.36, 12.40, has a *significance* of 0.01, by which we mean that 12.35 implies a measurement nearer to 12.35 than to 12.34 or 12.36, or lying in the interval $12.345 \leq x < 12.355$.

Similarly 5.5, 6.0, 7.0, 6.5, 5.5, would indicate a significance of 0.5. When very few measurements are available their significance is not obvious and it may be necessary to state it explicitly. Thus 12.0 (significance 0.5) can be distinguished from 12.0 (significance 0.1).

As a working rule we may assume that, unless otherwise stated, a number has a significance equal to a single unit in the last figure given. It is pointless and even misleading to use unnecessary decimal places, even zeros. For example 12.0 (significance 1.0) gives no more information than 12 (significance 1) which can be shortened to simply 12 according to our working rule. To give this measurement as 12.0 would incorrectly imply 12.0 (significance 0.1).

1.5.7 (See page 9)

When $F_n(x)$ is used for a discrete distribution it has no real physical significance for values of x other than $x_1, x_2, \ldots$. Nevertheless the smooth curve is particularly useful if it has a simple mathematical form.

1.5.8 (See page 12)

Even apparently precise quantities like mass, when looked at from the modern viewpoint of quantum mechanics, are seen to have an intrinsic 'spread' of values. However, such effects are quite imperceptible except for some experiments in the fields of nuclear and sub-nuclear physics.

1.6 PROBLEMS

1. An optical system measures length by counting electronically the number of light fringes passing a slit. Three series of measurements of the same length were as follows:

No. of fringes counted (in excess of 17 000)	No. of counts		
	A	B	C
243	0	3	16
244	1	7	60
245	2	15	135
246	2	15	180
247	3	18	194
248	1	14	187
249	0	12	138
250	1	8	64
251	0	4	18
252	0	4	8

Plot these results in normalized form and calculate the mean value for each series. Draw a smooth curve to represent series C and describe its general form.

2. Twenty-five measurements of the volume of a container were

17.462 17.517 17.483 17.490 17.464 17.485 17.520 17.476
17.478 17.492 17.501 17.488 17.497 17.510 17.509 17.485
17.473 17.515 17.466 17.507 17.483 17.491 17.476 17.505
17.490 cm^3.

Present these results as a normalized histogram (i) with intervals of 0.01 cm^3, (ii) with intervals of 0.02 cm^3.

3. Over a period of twenty years annual rainfall records were as follows:

Rainfall (cm). (1941) 89, (1942) 84, (1943) 85, (1944) 84, (1945) 75, (1946) 84, (1947) 73, (1948) 75, (1949) 81, (1950) 84, (1951) 82, (1952) 80, (1953) 80, (1954) 78, (1955) 82, (1956) 79, (1957) 80, (1958) 78, (1959) 80, (1960) 77.

Construct histograms to show these results (i) directly, and (ii) as ten-year averages starting with 1950 (the ten-year average for 1950 is the average over the years 1941 to 1950 inclusive). What is the magnitude of a typical fluctuation from one year to another in the two cases? Why is one smaller than the other?

4. Separate experiments to measure the lengths of roads A, B and C, each involving a very large number of measurements, gave the following frequency distributions in 1 m intervals:

Length (m)	Fraction of measurements (m^{-1})		
	A	B	C
2 760 ⎱ 2 761 ⎰	0.002	—	0.028
2 761 ⎱ 2 762 ⎰	0.009	—	0.110
2 762 ⎱ 2 763 ⎰	0.028	—	0.148
2 763 ⎱ 2 764 ⎰	0.066	—	0.160
2 764 ⎱ 2 765 ⎰	0.121	—	0.156
2 765 ⎱ 2 766 ⎰	0.174	—	0.138
2 766 ⎱ 2 767 ⎰	0.200	0.007	0.106
2 767 ⎱ 2 768 ⎰	0.174	0.066	0.071
2 768 ⎱ 2 769 ⎰	0.121	0.233	0.046
2 769 ⎱ 2 770 ⎰	0.066	0.388	0.022
2 770 ⎱ 2 771 ⎰	0.028	0.233	0.010
2 771 ⎱ 2 772 ⎰	0.009	0.066	0.004
2 772 ⎱ 2 773 ⎰	0.002	0.007	0.001

Construct the histograms for these results and calculate the best values and the standard deviations. Which is the most precise of the methods? Would you have any reservations about C?

5. A and B observe light flashes to the North. A believes there is only one source of these, while B believes there are two. The bearings of each of 15 successive flashes were measured, with the following results:

Direction (East of North); 10.72°, 11.05°, 11.36°, 10.74°, 11.16°, 10.85°, 10.92°, 11.18°, 10.96°, 10.63°, 11.02°, 11.26°, 10.64°, 10.95°, 11.13°.

Show these results, at the 5, 10 and 15 measurement stages, as normalized histograms with intervals 0.1° in width, starting from 10.5°.

Do you think that B's more elaborate explanation is justified by these results?

6. The observers in Problem 5 make a total of 200 measurements altogether. At the end of 100 and of 200 measurements the distributions were as follows:

	Numbers of measurements in 0.1° intervals									
	10.5 10.6	10.6 10.7	10.7 10.8	10.8 10.9	10.9 11.0	11.0 11.1	11.1 11.2	11.2 11.3	11.3 11.4	11.4 11.5
Total 100	1	7	13	9	6	24	24	10	5	1
Total 200	3	18	21	17	17	50	48	20	5	1

Construct the relevant histograms and compare them. Do you think a sufficiently clear shape is emerging from the measurements to back the opinion of A or of B against the other and, if so, whom would you support?

CHAPTER 2

Interpretation of results

In Chapter 1 we were led from the questions we asked about a typical experiment to consider the infinite experiment. This enabled us, in particular, to separate the precision of the apparatus from the value of the quantity we were measuring. In this chapter we shall use the insight we have gained to go back to the 'finite' experiment that, in practice, we have to interpret.

2.1 BEST ESTIMATE OF THE TRUE VALUE

When using the limiting frequency curve we are considering the results of an experimental measurement repeated an infinite number of times. In fact we can make only a finite number of independent measurements, n say, and can make only an *estimate* of the true value, not a certain and precise determination. Jenkins's first five measurements had a mean value

$$X_5 = (1.4 + 1.7 + 1.4 + 1.6 + 1.7)/5 = 1.56 \text{ sec}$$

but this is not necessarily X, the limiting value. However, at any stage

$$X_n = (x_1 + x_2 + \ldots + x_n)/n$$

is the mean we would calculate for the number of measurements then made, and is the number we expect to approach X as n increases. Now the simplest function of the numbers $x_1, \ldots, x_n$ which gives them all equal importance or reliability and which has the limiting value X *is* the mean. For this reason we define the *best* estimate of the mean of the infinitely repeated measurement as the mean of the finite number of measurements.

In a similar way we could talk of the best estimate of the mode or of the median value. Certain ambiguities can arise here, however. For example, Jenkins's five measurements do not have a single most frequently occurring value—both 1.4 and 1.7 sec occur twice.

The mean, however, is always uniquely defined and this is another reason, in the absence of arguments to the contrary, for using this and *defining the best estimate of a single number physical quantity, derived from n measurements of equal reliability,* $x_1, x_2, \ldots, x_n,$ *as the mean,*

[See §2.8.1, page 45; §2.8.2, page 46]

$$X_n = (x_1 + x_2 + \ldots + x_n)/n. \qquad (2.1)$$

2.2   BEST ESTIMATE OF PRECISION

The definition of the precision, like that of the true value of the quantity being measured, rests upon the notion of the infinitely repeated measurement. Once more we have to decide on a best estimate of this limiting number which can be calculated from a finite number of measurements.

At first sight we might think that from n measurements we should first calculate the mean (or best estimate of the true value),

$$X_n = (x_1 + x_2 + \ldots + x_n)/n;$$

then the *deviation* of each measurement from this,

$$\delta_1 = x_1 - X_n, \qquad \delta_2 = x_2 - X_n, \ldots, \qquad \delta_n = x_n - X_n;$$

and finally the *mean square deviation,*

$$\sigma_n^2 = (\delta_1^2 + \delta_2^2 + \ldots + \delta_n^2)/n.$$

The root mean square deviation, σ_n, has the limiting value σ as n increases, and appears to provide a reasonable best estimate for the precision.

There is, however, a flaw in this argument which, although unimportant for large values of n, is significant for small values, and involves a most important point of principle. If we put $n = 1$ we obtain for the best estimate of the true value

$$X_1 = x_1;$$

for the deviation

$$\delta_1 = 0;$$

and for the best estimate of precision

$$\sigma_1 = 0.$$

Now it is reasonable enough, in the absence of any information at all, other than the single measurement, to take this measurement as the best estimate of the true value. It is the *only* measurement and must, therefore, be the best.

On the other hand it is completely unreasonable to use this value alone to give also a best estimate of a second, independent quantity—the precision of the apparatus. No *one* number can ever give *two* pieces of independent information. One measurement gives no information whatsoever about the precision of the apparatus. If no other measurement is available we have to fall back on some other knowledge or assumption about the experiment if we wish to discuss its reliability. This was just the problem we faced at the beginning of Chapter 1 over comparing Robinson's 1.53 sec and Jenkins' 1.4 sec. We could not say how far we could trust either of these results without making some subjective judgments about Robinson or Jenkins, or—much better—asking for further measurements.

The *least* information that will yield an estimate of precision is *two* independent measurements x_i and x_j. These are sufficient to define a mean

$$X_{ij} = (x_i + x_j)/2;$$

the two (equal and opposite) deviations

$$\delta_{ij} = x_i - X_{ij}$$
$$\delta_{ji} = x_j - X_{ij};$$

and a mean square deviation

$$\Delta_{ij}^2 = (\delta_{ij}^2 + \delta_{ji}^2)/2.$$

Note that we are not committing here the error of trying to derive an excess of information from too little data. The last three quantities are not independent since, if $x_i > x_j$,

$$\Delta_{ij} = \delta_{ij} = -\delta_{ji} = (x_i - x_j)/2.$$

(If $x_i < x_j$ we simply have to change the sign of Δ_{ij}.) There are, therefore, only two independent quantities, X_{ij} and Δ_{ij}.

If n measurements $x_1, x_2, \ldots, x_n$ are available there are n ways of choosing x_i from among them, and this leaves $n - 1$ choices for x_j. So the number of ways of choosing two results x_i, x_j is $n(n - 1)$. Actually, each pair is then chosen twice, once as x_i, x_j and once as x_j, x_i, but in the equations which follow this 'double counting' occurs on each side and does not, therefore, affect the result—you can put in the factor $\frac{1}{2}$ on both sides of the equation if you like. Thus from the n measurements we can derive $n(n - 1)$ mean values X_{ij} and the arithmetic mean of these, X'_n, would be defined by

$$n(n-1)X'_n = \sum_{\substack{i=1 \\ (i \neq j)}}^{n} \sum_{j=1}^{n} (x_i + x_j)/2$$

$$= \tfrac{1}{2} \sum_{i=1}^{n} [(x_i + x_1) + \ldots + (x_i + x_{i-1}) + (x_i + x_{i+1})$$

$$+ \ldots + (x_i + x_n)]$$

$$= \tfrac{1}{2} \sum_{i=1}^{n} [(n-2)x_i + (x_1 + x_2 + \ldots + x_i + \ldots + x_n)]$$

$$= \tfrac{1}{2} \sum_{i=1}^{n} [(n-2)x_i + nX_n]$$

$$= \tfrac{1}{2}[(n-2)nX_n + n^2 X_n]$$

$$= n(n-1)X_n.$$

Thus

$$X'_n = X_n = (x_1 + x_2 + \ldots + x_n)/n,$$

so this rather elaborate way of defining a mean gives exactly the same value as the more simply defined mean we have already decided to use as the best estimate of the true value.

The estimate of precision is, however, a different matter. The mean, Δ_n^2, of the $n(n-1)$ squared deviations Δ_{ij}^2 is given by

$$n(n-1)\Delta_n^2 = \sum_{\substack{i=1 \\ (i \neq j)}}^{n} \sum_{j=1}^{n} \Delta_{ij}^2.$$

Now

$$\Delta_{ij}^2 = \tfrac{1}{4}(x_i - x_j)^2 = \tfrac{1}{4}(\delta_i - \delta_j)^2 = \tfrac{1}{4}(\delta_i^2 + \delta_j^2 - 2\delta_i \delta_j),$$

and as

$$\Delta_{ii}^2 = 0,$$

we may take the summations to include $i = j$. Then

$$n(n-1)\Delta_n^2 = \tfrac{1}{4} \sum_{i=1}^{n} \sum_{j=1}^{n} (\delta_i^2 + \delta_j^2 - 2\delta_i \delta_j)$$

$$= \tfrac{1}{4} \sum_{i=1}^{n} [n\delta_i^2 + (\delta_1^2 + \delta_2^2 + \ldots + \delta_n^2)$$

$$- 2\delta_i(\delta_1 + \delta_2 + \ldots + \delta_n)].$$

Now

$$\delta_1^2 + \delta_2^2 + \ldots + \delta_n^2 = n\sigma_n^2$$

and

$$\delta_1 + \delta_2 + \ldots + \delta_n = (x_1 - X_n) + (x_2 - X_n) + \ldots + (x_n - X_n) = 0.$$

Hence

$$n(n-1)\Delta_n^2 = n/4 \sum_{i=1}^{n} (\delta_i^2 + \sigma_n^2)$$

$$= n/4 \sum_{i=1}^{n} \delta_i^2 + n^2\sigma_n^2/4$$

$$= n^2\sigma_n^2/2,$$

or

$$2\Delta_n^2 = n\sigma_n^2/(n-1).$$

Thus $2\Delta_n^2$ is certainly *a* measure of the width of the frequency distribution from a finite experiment. If we define the '*adjusted*' *root mean square deviation*, s_n, by

$$s_n^2 = 2\Delta_n^2 = n\sigma_n^2/(n-1)$$

$$= (\delta_1^2 + \delta_2^2 + \ldots + \delta_n^2)/(n-1)$$

[See §2.8.3, page 47]

$$= [(x_1 - X_n)^2 + (x_2 - X_n)^2 + \ldots + (x_n - X_n)^2]/(n-1),$$

$$(2.2)$$

this is a quantity which has the meaningless value 0/0 (and therefore is not defined) for one observation only; is readily calculable for two or more measurements; and has for its limit as the number of measurements approaches infinity,

$$\lim_{n \to \infty} s_n = \lim_{n \to \infty} \sigma_n = \sigma.$$

s_n then, although defined in a very similar manner to σ_n and very nearly equal to it for large numbers of measurements, clearly gives a more reasonable interpretation of an experiment involving very few measurements. We shall therefore adopt s_n as the *best estimate of σ*, the precision of the apparatus.

2.3 COMBINATIONS OF MEASUREMENTS: TRUE VALUE AND PRECISION

It may happen that the physical quantity that we are interested in is not measured directly, but is a function of one or more different measurements made in an experiment. For example, if we wished to find the distance between two towns from a map, the distance we measure on the map would have to be multiplied by the map scale factor to give the actual distance. Or we might need the area of a rectangle, the lengths of whose sides we could measure. Here two separate measurements would have to be multiplied together to give the quantity of interest.

In such cases we must see how the true value and the precision for the final result depend upon the values of these quantities for the measurements actually made. Some simple cases are as follows.

2.3.1   Scale factor $(z = ax)$

The n measurements $x_1, x_2, \ldots, x_n$ give the n values of z:

$$z_1 = ax_1, \qquad z_2 = ax_2, \quad \ldots, \quad z_n = ax_n.$$

From these we calculate the mean,

$$\begin{aligned}
Z_n &= (z_1 + z_2 + \ldots + z_n)/n \\
&= a(x_1 + x_2 + \ldots + x_n)/n \\
&= aX_n,
\end{aligned}$$

which has the limiting value to be expected,

$$Z = aX.$$

The deviations in z are

$$\begin{aligned}
\omega_1 &= z_1 - Z_n = a(x_1 - X_n) = a\delta_1 \\
\omega_2 &= a\delta_2 \\
&\quad\vdots \\
\omega_n &= a\delta_n.
\end{aligned}$$

These give the mean square deviation of z,

$$\begin{aligned}
\sigma_n^2(z) &= (\omega_1^2 + \omega_2^2 + \ldots + \omega_n^2)/n \\
&= a^2(\delta_1^2 + \delta_2^2 + \ldots + \delta_n^2)/n \\
&= a^2\sigma_n^2(x).
\end{aligned}$$

So the standard deviation and its best estimate, the adjusted root mean square deviation, are

$$\sigma(z) = a\sigma(x)$$

$$s_n(z) = [n/(n-1)]^{\frac{1}{2}}\sigma_n(z) = as_n(x).$$

2.3.2   Sum $(z = x + y)$

Suppose we have n measurements $x_1, x_2, \ldots, x_n$ of x and m measurements $y_1, y_2, \ldots, y_m$ of y.

If the two sets are quite independent, any of the x_i can be combined with any of the y_i to give nm equally significant values of z,

$$z_{ij} = x_i + y_j.$$

The mean is

$$Z_{nm} = \frac{1}{nm} \sum_{i=1}^{n} \sum_{j=1}^{m} (x_i + y_j)$$

$$= \frac{1}{nm} \sum_{i=1}^{n} [mx_i + (y_1 + y_2 + \ldots + y_m)]$$

$$= \frac{1}{n} \sum_{i=1}^{n} (x_i + Y_m)$$

$$= [(x_1 + x_2 + \ldots + x_n) + nY_m]/n$$

$$= X_n + Y_m,$$

and the true value is

$$Z = X + Y.$$

The nm deviations are

$$\omega_{ij} = z_{ij} - Z_{nm}$$

$$= (x_i + y_j) - (X_n + Y_m)$$

$$= \delta_i + \gamma_j,$$

where δ_i and γ_j are the deviations of x_i and y_j. Hence the mean square deviation of z is given by

$$\sigma_{nm}^2(z) = \frac{1}{nm} \sum_{i=1}^{n} \sum_{j=1}^{m} \omega_{ij}^2$$

$$= \frac{1}{nm} \sum_{i=1}^{n} \sum_{j=1}^{m} (\delta_i^2 + \gamma_j^2 + 2\delta_i \gamma_j)$$

$$= \frac{1}{nm} \sum_{i=1}^{n} [m\delta_i^2 + (\gamma_1^2 + \gamma_2^2 + \ldots + \gamma_m^2)$$

$$+ 2\delta_i(\gamma_1 + \gamma_2 + \ldots + \gamma_m)]$$

$$= \frac{1}{n} \sum_{i=1}^{n} [\delta_i^2 + \sigma_m^2(y)]$$

$$= [(\delta_1^2 + \delta_2^2 + \ldots + \delta_n^2) + n\sigma_m^2(y)]/n$$

$$= \sigma_n^2(x) + \sigma_m^2(y),$$

and therefore the standard deviation is

$$\sigma(z) = [\sigma^2(x) + \sigma^2(y)]^{\frac{1}{2}}.$$

Note that the best estimate of the standard deviation is the adjusted value,

$$s_{nm}(z) = [s_n^2(x) + s_m^2(y)]^{\frac{1}{2}}$$
$$= [n\sigma_n^2(x)/(n-1) + m\sigma_m^2(y)/(m-1)]^{\frac{1}{2}}$$

which is still undefined and meaningless for $n = 1$ or $m = 1$.

2.3.3 Linear combination $(z = \alpha + ax + by + \ldots)$

This can be dealt with by combining the results of Sections 2.3.1 and 2.3.2. The algebra is straightforward though tedious and will not be given here. The results are, if $x, y, \ldots$ are measured $n, m, \ldots$ times respectively,

$$Z_{nm\ldots} = \alpha + aX_n + bY_m + \ldots,$$
$$Z = \alpha + aX + bY + \ldots, \tag{2.3}$$

$$\sigma_{nm\ldots}(z) = [a^2\sigma_n^2(x) + b^2\sigma_m^2(y) + \ldots]^{\frac{1}{2}},$$
$$\sigma(z) = [a^2\sigma^2(x) + b^2\sigma^2(y) + \ldots]^{\frac{1}{2}}, \tag{2.4}$$

$$s_{nm\ldots}(z) = [na^2\sigma_n^2(x)/(n-1) + mb^2\sigma_m^2(y)/(m-1) + \ldots]^{\frac{1}{2}}$$
$$= [a^2 s_n^2(x) + b^2 s_m^2(y) + \ldots]^{\frac{1}{2}}. \tag{2.5}$$

[See §2.8.4 page 49]

Note that any of the scale factors $a, b, \ldots$ may be negative. The sign, of course, affects the mean and the true value, but in the expressions for the precision of the overall experiment the contribution from each of the measurements adds a positive amount.

2.3.4 Logarithmic function $(z = \log x)$

The estimate of z arising from a typical measurement x_i is

$$z_i = \log x_i = \log(X_n + \delta_i)$$
$$= \log X_n + \log(1 + \delta/X_n)$$
$$= \log X_n + \delta_i/X_n - \delta_i^2/(2X_n^2) + \ldots. \tag{2.6}$$

From n measurements

$$nZ_n = z_1 + z_2 + \ldots + z_n$$
$$= n\log X_n - (\delta_1^2 + \delta_2^2 + \ldots + \delta_n^2)/(2X_n^2) + \ldots$$
$$= n\log X_n - n\sigma_n^2(x)/(2X_n^2) + \ldots. \tag{2.7}$$

The deviation of z_i is then, from Equations 2.6 and 2.7,

$$\omega_i = z_i - Z_n = \delta_i/X_n + [\sigma_n^2(x) - \delta_i^2]/(2X_n^2) + \ldots \qquad (2.8)$$

So, if $\sigma_n^2(x)/X_n^2$ and succeeding terms can be neglected,

$$Z_n = \log X_n,$$
$$Z = \log X,$$
$$\sigma_n(z) = [(\omega_1^2 + \omega_2^2 + \ldots + \omega_n^2)/n]^{\frac{1}{2}}$$
$$= \{[(\delta_1/X_n)^2 + (\delta_2/X_n)^2 + \ldots + (\delta_n/X_n)^2]/n\}^{\frac{1}{2}}$$
$$= \sigma_n(x)/X_n,$$
$$\sigma(z) = \sigma(x)/X,$$

[See §2.8.5, page 50]
$$s_n(z) = s_n(x)/X_n.$$

Note that it is the fractional deviation in the measured quality, δ_i/X_n, which enters into these expressions.

2.3.5   General product ($z = \alpha x^a y^b \ldots$)

This can be treated by first taking logarithms,

$$p = \log(z/\alpha) = a \log x + b \log y + \ldots$$

and then applying sections 2.3.4 and 2.3.3;

$$P_{nm\ldots} = \log(Z_{nm\ldots}/\alpha) = a \log X_n + b \log Y_m + \ldots,$$
$$\sigma_{nm\ldots}^2(p) = \sigma_{nm\ldots}^2(z)/Z_{nm\ldots}^2 = a^2\sigma_n^2(x)/X_n^2 + b^2\sigma_m^2(y)/Y_m^2 + \ldots.$$

Hence

$$Z_{nm\ldots} = \alpha X_n^a Y_m^b \ldots,$$
$$Z = \alpha X^a Y^b \ldots \qquad (2.9)$$

and

$$\sigma_{nm\ldots}(z)/Z_{nm\ldots} = [a^2\sigma_n^2(x)/X_n^2 + b^2\sigma_m^2(y)/Y_m^2 + \ldots]^{\frac{1}{2}},$$
$$\sigma(z)/Z = [a^2\sigma^2(x)/X^2 + b^2\sigma^2(y)/Y^2 + \ldots]^{\frac{1}{2}}, \qquad (2.10)$$
$$s_{nm\ldots}(z)/Z_{nm\ldots} = \{na^2\sigma_n^2(x)/[(n-1)X_n^2] + mb^2\sigma_m^2(y)/$$

[See §2.8.6, page 50]
$$[(m-1)Y_m^2] + \ldots\}^{\frac{1}{2}}$$
$$= [a^2 s_n^2(x)/X_n^2 + b^2 s_m^2(y)/Y_m^2 + \ldots]^{\frac{1}{2}}. \qquad (2.11)$$

Note that the qualities involving errors all occur in *fractional* or *proportional* or *relative* form. More complicated functions can often be treated by applying successively the results of two or more of sections 2.3.1 to 2.3.5. If this is not possible the analysis may become rather involved, but the following simple approach is sometimes adequate.

2.3.6   General function $(z = f(x))$

We shall suppose that $f(x)$ is 'well-behaved', that is, continuous and differentiable as many times as we require over the range of variables involved in the experiment. Then if δz is the increment in z corresponding to an increment δx in x, we may use the following expansion:

$$z + \delta z = f(x + \delta x)$$
$$= f(x) + \delta x\, df(x)/dx + \tfrac{1}{2}(\delta x)^2\, d^2 f(x)/dx^2 + \ldots.$$

Hence if $x_1, x_2, \ldots, x_n$ are independent measurements of x, with mean X_n, a typical estimate of z is

$$z_i = f(x_i)$$
$$= f(X_n + \delta_i)$$
$$= f(X_n) + f'(X_n)\delta_i + \tfrac{1}{2}f''(X_n)\delta_i^2 + \ldots, \qquad (2.12)$$

where $f'(X_n)$ stands for $df(x)/dx$ at $x = X_n$, etc.

The mean of the n values for z is

$$Z_n = \sum_i z_i/n$$
$$= \sum_i [f(X_n) + f'(X_n)\delta_i + \tfrac{1}{2}f''(X_n)\delta_i^2 + \ldots]/n$$
$$= f(X_n) + \tfrac{1}{2}f''(X_n)\sigma_n^2(x) + \ldots.$$

So, provided $f''(X_n)\sigma_n^2(x)$ and succeeding terms are negligible compared with $f(X_n)$,

$$Z_n = f(X_n). \qquad (2.13)$$

The deviations in z are now, from Equations 2.12 and 2.13,

$$\omega_i = z_i - Z_n$$
$$= \delta_i[f'(X_n) + \tfrac{1}{2}f''(X_n)\delta_i + \ldots].$$

Then

$$\sigma_n^2(z) = \sum_i \omega_i^2/n$$
$$= \sum_i \delta_i^2 [f'^2(X_n) + f'(X_n)f''(X_n)\delta_i + \ldots]/n,$$

and if $f'(X_n)f''(X_n)\Sigma\delta_i^3$ and succeeding terms are negligible compared with $f'^2(X_n)\Sigma\delta_i^2$,

$$\sigma_n^2(z) = \sum_i f'^2(X_n)\delta_i^2/n = f'^2(X_n)\sigma_n^2(x)$$

or

$$\sigma_n(z) = f'(X_n)\sigma_n(x),$$
$$\sigma(z) = f'(X)\sigma(x) \tag{2.14}$$

and

$$s_n(z) = f'(X_n)s_n(x). \tag{2.15}$$

Note that we have used a circular argument here. We assume something about X_n—the comparative magnitude of various differential coefficients at $x = X_n$—in order to use X_n for calculating Z_n. If these assumptions turn out to be true for this calculated value, we may accept it. But if not, we may be in trouble.

[See §2.8.7, page 51]

2.3.7 General function of several variables $(z = f(x, y, \ldots))$

For this we use the expansion which states that, when f is 'well-behaved' in all its variables, increments $\delta x, \delta y, \ldots$ in them will change z to

$$z + \delta z = f(x, y, \ldots.) + \delta x f_x + \delta y f_y + \ldots$$
$$+ \tfrac{1}{2}(\delta x)^2 f_{xx} + \delta x \delta y f_{xy} + \tfrac{1}{2}(\delta y)^2 f_{yy} + \ldots,$$

where $f_x, f_y, \ldots, f_{xx}, f_{xy}, f_{yy}, \ldots$ denote the values of the partial derivatives $\partial f/\partial x$, $\partial f/\partial y, \ldots$, $\partial^2 f/\partial x^2$, $\partial^2 f/\partial x \partial y$, $\partial^2 f/\partial y^2, \ldots$ at $(x, y, \ldots)$.

Suppose n measurements are made of x, with mean X_n and mean square deviation $\sigma_n(x)$; m of y, with mean Y_m and mean square deviation $\sigma_m(y)$; $\ldots$. Then typical measurements $x_i, y_j, \ldots$ will give z a deviation $\omega_{ij} \ldots$ from its mean, where

$$\omega_{ij} = \delta_i f_x + \nu_j f_y + \ldots + \tfrac{1}{2}\delta_i^2 f_{xx} + \ldots,$$
$$\delta_i = x_i - X_n, \qquad \nu_j = y_j - Y_m, \ldots$$

are the deviations of each measurement from its mean, and the partial derivatives $f_x, f_y, \ldots, f_{xx}, \ldots$ are all evaluated at $(X_n, Y_m, \ldots)$.

Following arguments similar to those of sections 2.3.3 and 2.3.6 we find the mean value of z to be

$$Z_{nm\ldots} = f(X_n, Y_m, \ldots) \tag{2.16}$$

and the standard error

$$s_{nm...}(z) = [nf_x^2\sigma_n^2(x)/(n-1) + mf_y^2\sigma_m^2(y)/(m-1) + ...]^{\frac{1}{2}}$$
$$= [f_x^2 s_n^2(x) + f_y^2 s_m^2(y) + ...]^{\frac{1}{2}}. \qquad (2.17)$$

These, like the results of the preceding section, are approximations requiring the deviations to be sufficiently small for terms such as $\sigma_n^2(x)f_{xx}$ and $\delta_i^2\nu_{ij}f_xf_{xy}$ to be neglected in the series expansions from which $Z_{nm...}$ and $s_{nm...}(z)$ are derived. This is equivalent to regarding z as varying only linearly with $x, y, ...$ over the ranges of the measured quantities.

It may be noted that when the conditions for this section to be true are met, the results of sections 2.3.1 to 2.3.6 may then be derived as particular cases.

2.4 ACCURACY OF THE MEAN VALUE: STANDARD ERROR

We now come to a rather more involved problem. We know (or rather, assume) that the mean, X_n, approaches the true value, X, in the limit as n becomes infinitely large. This is one reason why we have chosen it as the best estimate of the true value that can be contained from a finite number of measurements.

Can we go farther and say *how* good an estimate X_n is? In otherwords, how accurately is X_n an estimate of X?

A small number of measurements will show a frequency distribution that is a rough approximation to the limiting frequency curve characteristic of the apparatus. Clearly if this has a narrow symmetrical peak, and therefore a small value of σ, the measurements are likely to be close together and their mean, X_n, will be near the true value X. If the peak is broad the measurements will be more widely scattered and X_n is less likely to be near X. So σ, or its best estimate s_n, must describe the accuracy of X_n to the extent that the smaller s_n is, the nearer X_n is likely to be to X.

On the other hand, since we believe that X_n approaches X as n increases, this means that by making n large enough we can obtain a value of X_n as near X as we like. So, even when the apparatus has a poor precision (large s_n, or σ), we can achieve any desired degree of accuracy in the estimated true value by making a sufficient number of measurements.

If enough measurements are made for X_n to be near X, and therefore to be an accurate estimate of X, we should expect X_n not to fluctuate very much as the group of measurements by which it is defined is varied. These fluctuations would show up if we repeatedly made groups of n measurements, each yielding a value for the mean,

$$X_n = (x_1 + x_2 + \ldots + x_n)/n.$$

If we rewrite this as

$$X_n = x_1/n + x_2/n + \ldots + x_n/n$$

we can think of X_n as a quantity which is itself the sum of the measurements $x_1/n, x_2/n, \ldots, x_n/n$. The results of section 2.3.3 can therefore be used to give the standard deviation of X_n,

$$\sigma(X_n) = [\sigma^2(x_1)/n^2 + \sigma^2(x_2)/n^2 + \ldots + \sigma^2(x_n)/n^2]^{\frac{1}{2}}.$$

But

$$\sigma^2(x_1) = \sigma^2(x_2) = \ldots = \sigma^2(x_n) = \sigma^2(x),$$

since $x_1, x_2, \ldots, x_n$ are all measurements of the same quantity. Thus

$$\sigma(X_n) = \sigma(x)/n^{\frac{1}{2}}. \tag{2.18}$$

The best estimate of $\sigma(x)$ is

$$s_n = (\delta_1^2 + \delta_2^2 + \ldots + \delta_n^2)^{\frac{1}{2}}/(n-1)^{\frac{1}{2}}.$$

Hence the best estimate of $\sigma(X_n)$ is

$$\begin{aligned}
S_n &= (\delta_1^2 + \delta_2^2 + \ldots + \delta_n^2)^{\frac{1}{2}}/[n(n-1)]^{\frac{1}{2}} \\
&= \sigma_n(x)/(n-1)^{\frac{1}{2}} \\
&= s_n(x)/n^{\frac{1}{2}}. \tag{2.19}
\end{aligned}$$

Just as we took the width of the distribution for single measurements, x, as a measure of precision for the apparatus, to tell us how close to the true value a single measurement is likely to be, so the width of the distribution for the mean, X_n, tells us how accurately n measurements are likely to give the true value. $\sigma(X_n)$ is the *standard error* and its best estimate, S_n, is the *adjusted standard error*. The results of an experiment may be summarized in the form

$$X = X_n \pm S_n. \tag{2.20}$$

We may note the following:

1. S_n is not a third quantity independent of s_n and X_n, although it depends in a much more explicit way on the number of measurements.

2. S_n involves both the intrinsic accuracy of the apparatus ($\sigma(x)$ or $\sigma_n(x)$) and the number of measurements (n) in a way that we would expect—the accuracy of the mean increases as the intrinsic accuracy increases *and* as the number of measurements increases.

3. The improvement in accuracy with number of measurements goes only as $n^{-\frac{1}{2}}$ (for large values of n). Consequently although the poor intrinsic precision of an experiment can be overcome by repeating the measurements sufficiently often, the effort might well be better spent in improving the intrinsic accuracy. Suppose, for example, that 10 measurements yielded an accuracy of the mean of a time

$$S_n = 0.1 \text{ sec.}$$

To improve this tenfold with the same apparatus, that is to achieve

$$S_n = 0.01 \text{ sec,}$$

would require 1000 measurements. However the same result could be obtained instead, still with only 10 measurements, if the precision of the apparatus, $\sigma(x)$, were improved to $\frac{1}{10}$ of its initial value.

It is most important to recognize the difference between the best estimate of *precision* s_n, and the best estimate of *error* S_n. As the number of measurements, n, increases s_n *does not decrease*—it simply approaches closer and closer to the fixed non-zero quantity σ which defines the precision of the experiment, and which may be large or small, depending upon the nature of that experiment. S_n, however, *does decrease* as n increases—it estimates the mean deviation of X_n from X, the true value, and this deviation, from our definition of true value, must approach zero as n is increased towards infinity.

2.5   ACCURACY OF THE STANDARD DEVIATION: NUMBER OF SIGNIFICANT FIGURES

The standard error, or its best estimate S_n, is our measure of the accuracy with which the mean, X_n, estimates the true value, X. We shall see later (sections 5.3 and 6.3) that this means, for most experiments, that the true value is roughly twice as likely to fall within the interval $(X_n - S_n, X_n + S_n)$ as outside it. S_n is proportional to the root mean square deviation, σ_n, and both of these will fluctuate according to the group of n measurements from which they are derived, just as X_n itself does.

So the interval in which we expect the true value to lie is itself subject to error and to estimate this we must estimate the standard deviation of S_n or of σ_n. Of course we could go farther and estimate the standard deviation of this estimate and so on indefinitely at prodigious, and probably unjustified, labour and cost. Nevertheless, if we do go one stage farther than we have done so far and estimate the standard deviation of S_n, that is $\sigma(S_n)$, we shall have a useful practical guide to a question that often occurs—how many significant figures should be recorded and calculated?

From section 2.3.6 we have

$$\begin{aligned} 2S_n\sigma(S_n) &= \sigma(S_n^2) \\ &= \sigma[\sigma_n^2/(n-1)] \\ &= \frac{1}{n(n-1)}\,\sigma(\delta_1^2 + \delta_2^2 + \ldots + \delta_n^2). \end{aligned}$$

Since $\delta_1^2, \delta_2^2, \ldots, \delta_n^2$ are derived from measurements of the same quantity, the standard deviation of each of them will be the same. If we denote it by $\sigma(\delta^2)$, then from Equation 2.4,

$$2S_n\sigma(S_n) = \frac{\sigma(\delta^2)}{n^{\frac{1}{2}}(n-1)}. \tag{2.21}$$

We therefore need to know the width of the frequency distribution of δ^2. We know something about the limiting form of this already. δ^2 cannot be less than zero, its most probable value is zero (assuming the distribution curve for x is single-peaked), and its mean value is, by definition, σ^2. It will therefore be of the form shown in figure 2.1.

It must be emphasized, however, that the knowledge we have does *not* determine the shape, and, in particular, the width, $\sigma(\delta^2)$, of this curve. σ^2 does not fix this any more than X fixes the width, σ, of the frequency distribution of x. In principle it is an independent quantity that has to be separately calculated from the experimental results.

Nevertheless, if we are prepared to abandon any pretence at mathematical rigour we can make a reasonable shot at an order of magnitude estimate which is adequate for our purposes. What we might call the 'left-hand half-width' (that is the spread in δ^2 from the mean σ^2 to the sharp left-hand edge of the curve) is σ^2. The tail of values of δ^2 to the right must decrease to a negligible magnitude beyond, say, $3\sigma^2$ or $4\sigma^2$ from the mean, otherwise σ^2

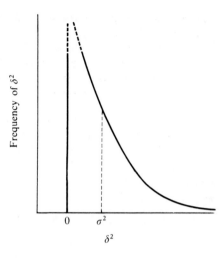

Figure 2.1

could hardly be the mean value for the distribution. So the 'right-hand half-width' will also be about σ^2 in size. Then the 'width' of the frequency distribution of δ^2 will be of the order of σ^2, or

$$\sigma(\delta^2) \sim \sigma^2,$$

by which we mean that the equality is correct to within a factor of $\frac{1}{3}$ to 3, say. Of course it is perfectly possible to invent a peculiar curve for which this result is not true, but it would have to be a peculiar experiment that would give rise to it.

To the accuracy of this result we can now rewrite Equation 2.21 as

$$S_n \sigma(S_n) \sim \sigma^2/n^{\frac{3}{2}}.$$

But, from Equation 2.17,

$$S_n \simeq \sigma_n/n^{\frac{1}{2}}$$

and

$$\sigma \simeq \sigma_n.$$

Hence

$$\sigma(S_n) \sim \sigma_n/n \sim S_n/n^{\frac{1}{2}}.$$

In view of the method we used to derive this result, the factor $n^{-\frac{1}{2}}$ must not be taken too literally. While it is satisfactory for large n, it will not be true for small n for the same sort of reason that was discussed in section 2.2. There we saw that at least two measurements were necessary to determine estimates of the independent quantities X and σ. To estimate a third independent quantity, $\sigma(S_n)$, a maximum of three measurements is required, so that $S_n/(n-2)^{\frac{1}{2}}$ would be a more prudent estimate for the standard deviation of S_n.

We can see that the relative accuracy of S_n,

$$\sigma(S_n)/S_n \sim 1/(n-2)^{\frac{1}{2}}, \qquad (2.22)$$

gives a quantitative basis for deciding how many figures to retain in an experimental result.

Thus if 100 measurements give values

$$X_n = 17.386, \qquad s_n = 1.226, \qquad S_n = 0.1226,$$

the relative accuracy of S_n is around 10%. In other words the true value of S_n has a roughly $2:1$ chance of lying within the interval 0.11034 and 0.13486. It is clear that the third and fourth figures in s_n and S_n are of no practical significance, and that even the second is in some doubt.

An adequate summary of the result would be

$$X = 17.39 \pm 0.13,$$

where the standard error is given to two figures, and X_n is adjusted to the same significant figure; it is probably true that even

$$X = 17.40 \pm 0.15$$

would lose little worthwhile information from the experiment. Note that we have given the error in the last estimate to a significance of 0.05 and that in both cases the estimate of the error has been given to the nearest significant figure *above*—it is safer to overestimate rather than underestimate errors.

[See §2.8.8, page 55]

In any experiment involving ten or fewer measurements, where the errors are estimated solely from these, there is no point at all in giving the precision of the apparatus to more than two significant figures or the standard error of the final result to more than one figure.

2.6 COMBINATIONS OF MEASUREMENTS: STANDARD ERROR

We must now complete the results of section 2.3 by calculating the standard error of quantities which are themselves functions of measured quantities.

2.6.1   Linear combination ($z = \alpha + ax + by + \ldots$)

We know from section 2.3.3 that the mean from n measurements of x, m of y, etc., is

$$Z_{nm\ldots} = \alpha + aX_n + bY_m + \ldots.$$

The standard deviation of $Z_{nm\ldots}$ is, therefore,

$$\sigma(Z_{nm\ldots}) = [a^2\sigma^2(X_n) + b^2\sigma^2(Y_m) + \ldots]^{\frac{1}{2}}.$$

Now the best estimates of the standard deviations of X_n, Y_m, $\ldots$, are the standard errors $S_n(x)$, $S_m(y)$, etc. Hence the best estimate of the standard deviation of $Z_{nm\ldots}$, that is, the standard error for the quantity z arising from the n measurements of x, m of y, etc., is

$$s_{nm\ldots}(z) = [a^2S_n^2(x) + b^2S_m^2(y) + \ldots]^{\frac{1}{2}}$$
$$= [a^2\sigma_n^2(x)/(n-1) + b^2\sigma_m^2(y)/(m-1) + \ldots]^{\frac{1}{2}}. \quad (2.23)$$

[See §2.8.9, page 55]

2.6.2   General product ($z = \alpha x^a y^b \ldots$)

From section 2.3.5 the mean of the product is

$$Z_{nm\ldots} = \alpha X_n^a Y_m^b \ldots.$$

Then the standard error of z will have for its best estimate $S_{nm\ldots}$, where

$$S_{nm\ldots}(z)/Z_{nm\ldots} = [a^2S_n^2(x)/X_n^2 + b^2S_m^2(y)/Y_m^2 + \ldots]^{\frac{1}{2}}$$
$$= \{a^2\sigma_n^2(x)/[(n-1)X_n^2] + b^2\sigma_m^2(y)/$$
$$[(m-1)Y_m^2] + \ldots\}^{\frac{1}{2}}. \quad (2.24)$$

[See §2.8.10, page 56]

2.6.3   General function ($z = f(x)$)

From Equations 2.15 and 2.16 we obtain immediately

$$S_n(z) = f'(X_n)S_n(x). \quad (2.25)$$

2.6.4   General function of several variables ($z = f(x, y, \ldots)$)

For this we extend the result 2.25 to each of the variables concerned. Corresponding to the precision or standard error of Equation 2.17 we find that the standard error of the mean is

$$S_{nm\ldots}(z) = [f_x^2\sigma_n^2(x)/(n-1) + f_y^2\sigma_m^2(y)/(m-1) + \ldots]^{\frac{1}{2}}$$
$$= [f_x^2S_n^2(x) + f_y^2S_m^2(y) + \ldots]^{\frac{1}{2}}. \quad (2.26)$$

When an experiment requires two or more different quantities to be measured in order to find a third, the expression 2.26 gives useful guidance over the numbers of measurements and the precisions to be aimed at. As the separate squared errors are each multiplied by the square of the corresponding partial derivative it is clear that most care will probably be needed with the quantity having the largest partial derivative. It is important, therefore, to identify the latter and to see, perhaps with the aid of some rough preliminary measurements, with what precision the corresponding quantity may be measured. This will then tell us how well we need

[See §2.8.11, page 57] attempt to measure the other quantities in order to give comparable contributions to the overall standard error.

2.7 DISCUSSION OF JENKINS' AND ROBINSON'S EXPERIMENTS

We are now able to summarize the information from any experiment as three numbers—the mean, X_n, which is the best estimate of the quantity we are trying to measure; the adjusted root mean square deviation, s_n, which is the best estimate of the precision of the apparatus; and the adjusted standard error of the mean, S_n, which is the best estimate of the overall accuracy of the experiment in determining the quantity of interest.

If we calculate X_n, s_n and S_n at each stage of Jenkins' and Robinson's experiments we obtain the results given in Table 2.1.

Table 2.1

No. of measurements		Best estimate of true value X_n (sec)	Best estimate of precision s_n (sec)	Best estimate of standard error S_n (sec)
1	Jenkins	1.4	—	—
	Robinson	1.52	—	—
5	Jenkins	1.56	0.152 (0.15)	0.068 (0.07)
	Robinson	1.514	0.010 (0.010)	0.0046 (0.005)
500	Jenkins	1.5326 (1.533)	0.1626 (0.163)	0.0073 (0.007)

The numbers in brackets have been shortened in accordance with the discussion of section 2.5.

Table 2.1 enables us to answer some, at least, of the questions we asked at the beginning of this book. We can say:

1. After one measurement each Jenkins and Robinson gave two independent and different results. No information was availa-

ble on the precision of their apparatus or the accuracy of these results, so no comparison was possible.

2. After five measurements each, it appeared that Robinson's apparatus was some fifteen times more precise than Jenkins' (0.01 sec compared with 0.15 sec). Robinson's estimates of the true value of the period and of its standard error were 1.514 sec and 0.0005 sec, which we shall write as (1.514 ± 0.005) sec, compared with Jenkins' (1.56 ± 0.07) sec. So the accuracy of Robinson's estimate is more than ten times better than Jenkins', and clearly, if one has to be chosen, it would be Robinson's.

3. After Jenkins had increased his number of measurements to 500 the poor precision of his apparatus was confirmed. In fact it looks a little worse at this stage (0.163 sec compared with the earlier value of 0.15 sec), still somewhat over fifteen times less precise than Robinson's. However, his hard work has had an effect, for his value of (1.533 ± 0.007) sec for the true value bears a standard error 0.007 sec which, although rather greater than Robinson's 0.005 sec, is certainly not so different as to justify our disregarding his estimate completely in favour of Robinson's We might well feel that since the results are of comparable accuracy, and within 0.02 sec of each other, that the true value is somewhere between the two, perhaps a little nearer Robinson's because his is still the more accurate estimate of the two.

Just how to combine the results in a case like this is a matter we shall take up later. Before that we shall re-examine, in the next chapter, the results obtained so far to see whether there is some principle underlying them which will enable us to deal with the rather more complicated situations that often arise in experimental science and engineering.

[See §3.5, page 74; §3.6, page 77]

2.8   COMMENTS AND WORKED EXAMPLES

2.8.1 (See page 27)

We have already used $\bar{x}$ to denote the true value or mean of an 'infinite' number of measurements (section 1.3). This is a useful and common notation for the mean of any number of measurements and may be used also for the best estimate of the true value when it is clear that it refers to the mean of a finite number of measurements from an actual experiment. The Σ notation may also be used for summation, more or less elaborately expressed according to how obvious the meaning is from the context. Thus the conclusion of section 2.1 might be written in any of the following forms:

$$X_n = \bar{x}$$
$$= (x_1 + x_2 + \ldots + x_n)/n$$
$$= \sum_{i=1}^{n} x_i/n = \sum_i x_i/n = \sum x_i/n = \sum x/n. \qquad (2.27)$$

2.8.2 Example 3 (See page 27)

What is the best estimate of the true height of the building of Example 2 (page 21)?

The best estimate is the mean of the 16 measurements,

$$X_{16} = (33.478 + 33.457 + \ldots + 33.477)/16$$
$$= 33.488 \text{ m}.$$

A lot of unnecessary labour is involved if the 16 numbers are simply added together and then divided by 16. A method that is both simpler and less likely to cause arithmetical errors is to use an *assumed* or *guessed* or *false* mean. Thus if X_A is an assumed value for X_n, the mean, and $\delta_{iA} = x_i - X_A$ is the deviation of the ith measurement from this, then

$$X_n = (x_1 + x_2 + \ldots + x_n)/n$$
$$= [(X_A + \delta_{1A}) + (X_A + \delta_{2A}) + \ldots + (X_A + \delta_{nA})]/n$$
$$= [nX_A + (\delta_{1A} + \delta_{2A} + \ldots + \delta_{nA})]/n$$
$$= X_A + (\delta_{1A} + \delta_{2A} + \ldots + \delta_{nA})/n. \qquad (2.28)$$

If X_A is chosen near to X_n, the deviations, δ_{iA}, will be small numbers and therefore more easily summed than the x_i. Thus in the present example we might guess the mean to be 33.480 m we could then construct the following table:

$X_A = 33.480$ m

x_i(m)	33.478	33.457	33.492	33.499	33.490	33.512
δ_{iA}(m)	−0.002	−0.023	0.012	0.019	0.010	0.032
x_i(m)	33.475	33.504	33.473	33.482	33.492	33.501
δ_{iA}(m)	−0.005	0.024	−0.007	0.002	0.012	0.021
x_i(m)	33.470	33.509	33.502	33.477		
δ_{iA}(m)	−0.010	0.029	0.022	−0.003		

Then

$$\delta_{1A} + \delta_{2A} + \ldots + \delta_{16A}$$

$$= -0.002 - 0.023 + 0.012 + \ldots + 0.022 - 0.003$$

$$= (0.012 + 0.019 + 0.010 + 0.032 + 0.024$$
$$+ 0.002 + 0.012 + 0.021 + 0.029 + 0.022)$$
$$- (0.002 + 0.023 + 0.005 + 0.007 + 0.010 + 0.003)$$

$$= 0.183 - 0.050 = 0.133 \text{ m.}$$

Hence

$$X_{16} = 33.480 + 0.133/16$$
$$= 33.480 + 0.008$$
$$= 33.488 \text{ m.}$$

When X_A is near X_n the δ_{iA} will have both positive and negative values. If this is thought to be confusing it can be avoided by choosing X_A to be smaller than the smallest measurement. In the present example we could take 33.450 as the assumed mean. All the δ_{iA} would then be positive, but would be larger numbers than before.

It is a matter of personal preference whether the deviations δ_{iA} are to be as amall as possible or all of one sign. When even a simple calculator is available there is little to be gained by choosing X_A to give the smallest deviations. Indeed, there is least chance of error if X_A is chosen to make the calculation of the δ_{iA} as straightforward as possible. In this case $X_A = 33.400$ m or even $X_A = 33.000$ m would be a better choice.

2.8.3 (See page 30)

Once an assumed mean, X_A, and the deviations from it, δ_{iA}, have been used to calculate the mean, X_n, it is not necessary to recalculate the deviations, δ_i, from this in order to determine the mean square deviation, σ_n^2. For

$$\delta_i = x_i - X_n = x_i - X_A + X_A - X_n$$
$$= \delta_{iA} + \delta_A,$$

where

$$\delta_A = X_A - X_n$$

is the deviation of the assumed mean from the true mean. Then

$$\delta_i^2 = \delta_{iA}^2 + 2\delta_A\delta_{iA} + \delta_A^2$$

and

$$n\sigma_n^2 = \sum_i \delta_i^2 = \sum_i \delta_{iA}^2 + 2\delta_A \sum_i \delta_{iA} + n\delta_A^2.$$

But

$$\sum_i \delta_{iA} = \sum_i (\delta_i - \delta_A) = -n\delta_A.$$

Hence

$$n\sigma_n^2 = \sum_i \delta_{iA}^2 - n\delta_A^2 \tag{2.29}$$

and

$$s_n^2 = \sum_i \delta_{iA}^2/(n-1) - n\delta_A^2/(n-1). \tag{2.30}$$

The special case

$$X_A = 0 \quad \text{or} \quad \delta_i = x_i, \quad \delta_A = -X_n$$

gives expressions corresponding to Equation 1.12:

$$\sigma_n^2 = \sum_i x_i^2/n - X_n^2 = \overline{x^2} - (\bar{x})^2, \tag{2.31}$$

$$s_n^2 = n[\overline{x^2} - (\bar{x})^2]/(n-1). \tag{2.32}$$

EXAMPLE 4

What is the best estimate of the true height of the building and of the precision of the method used to give the measurements of Example 2 (page 21)?

We have already calculated the true height in Example 3 (page 46). However, we shall do so again, using a different assumed mean, and extend the calculation to give the precision as well.

$X_A = 33.450$ m

x_i(m)	33.478	33.457	33.492	33.499	33.490	33.512
$\delta_{iA} \times 10^3$(m)	28	7	42	49	40	62
$\delta_{iA}^2 \times 10^6$(m^2)	784	49	1764	2401	1600	3844

x_i(m)	33.475	33.504	33.473	33.482	33.492	33.501
$\delta_{iA} \times 10^3$(m)	25	54	23	32	42	51
$\delta_{iA}^2 \times 10^6$(m^2)	625	2916	529	1024	1764	2601

x_i(m)	33.470	33.509	33.502	33.477
$\delta_{iA} \times 10^3$(m)	20	59	52	27
$\delta_{iA}^2 \times 10^6$(m^2)	400	3481	2704	729

$$\sum_{i=1}^{16} \delta_{iA} = 613 \times 10^{-3}\,\text{m}$$

$$\sum_{i=1}^{16} \delta_{iA}^2 = 27215 \times 10^{-6}\,\text{m}^2.$$

Hence

$$X_{16} = 33.450 + 0.613/16$$
$$= 33.450 + 0.038$$
$$= 33.488\,\text{m},$$

$$\delta_A = X_A - X_{16} = -0.038\,\text{m}, \qquad \delta_A^2 = 0.001444\,\text{m}^2,$$
$$16\sigma_{16}^2 = 0.027215 - 16 \times 0.001444$$
$$= 0.027215 - 0.023104$$
$$= 0.004111\,\text{m}^2.$$

Hence

$$s_{16}^2 = 16\sigma_{16}^2/15 = 0.000274\,\text{m}^2, \qquad s_{16} = 0.0166\,\text{m}.$$

So the true height of the building is 33.488 m and the precision of the method of measurement is 0.0166 m.

2.8.4 Example 5 (See page 33)

Eight measurements of the volume of a block of iron had a mean value of 26.52 cm^3 and a mean square deviation 0.025 cm^6. Fifteen measurements of a block of aluminium gave the corresponding values 8.72 cm^3 and 0.058 cm^6. If the density of iron is 7.88 g cm^{-3} and of aluminium is 2.70 g cm^{-3}, what is the best estimate of the total mass of the two blocks and of the precision of the method of measurement?

If X is the true volume of the iron and Y that of the aluminium, the total mass Z would be given by

$$Z = 7.88X + 2.70Y.$$

The best estimate of X is

$$X_8 = 26.52\,\text{cm}^3$$

and of Y is

$$Y_{15} = 8.72 \text{ cm}^3.$$

Hence the best estimate of Z is, from Equation 2.3,

$$Z_{8\,15} = 7.88 \times 26.52 + 2.70 \times 8.72$$
$$= 232.5 \text{ g}.$$

The mean square deviation of the 'iron' measurements is

$$\sigma_8^2 = 0.025 \text{ cm}^6$$

and of the 'aluminium' measurements is

$$\sigma_{15}^2 = 0.058 \text{ cm}^6.$$

Hence, from Equation 2.5,

$$s_{8\,15}^2(z) = \tfrac{8}{7} \times 7.88^2 \times 0.0025 + \tfrac{15}{14} \times 2.70^2 \times 0.058$$
$$= 1.774 + 0.453$$
$$= 2.227 \text{ g}^2.$$

So

$$s_{8\,15}(z) = 1.493 \text{ g}$$

is the best estimate of precision.

2.8.5 (See page 34)

These results are obtained by retaining only the first terms of Equations 2.7 and 2.8. If we retain the first two terms to obtain a second, better, approximation we can see that Z_n and Z are somewhat displaced from $\log X_n$ and $\log X$ and that the frequency distribution of ω_i is not simply that of δ_i multiplied by the scale factor $1/X_n$. These points are considered further in section 2.8.7.

2.8.6   Example 6 (See page 34)

Six measurements of the length of a wire had a mean value of 527.3 cm with mean square deviation 0.01 cm^2. Twelve measurements of its diameter had a mean 0.062 cm and mean square deviation 1.2×10^{-6} cm^2. If the resistivity is known to be 44.2×10^{-6} ohm cm what is the best estimate of the resistance of the wire and of the precision of this method of determining it?

If l is the length of the wire and d is its diameter, then the resistance, r, is given by

$$r = 4\rho l/(\pi d^2)$$
$$= (4\rho/\pi)ld^{-2},$$

where ρ is the resistivity. With ρ as given we have

$$r = 56.28 \times 10^{-6}\, ld^{-2}.$$

The best estimate of l is

$$L_6 = 527.3 \text{ cm}$$

and of d is

$$D_{12} = 0.062 \text{ cm}.$$

Hence the best estimate of r is, from Equation 2.9,

$$R_{6\,12} = 56.28 \times 527.3 \times (0.062)^{-2} \times 10^{-6}$$
$$= 7.72 \text{ ohm}.$$

The adjusted mean square deviation for the length measurements is, from Equation 2.2,

$$s_6^2(l) = \tfrac{6}{5}\sigma_6^2(l) = 0.012 \text{ cm}^2$$

and its relative value is

$$[s_6(l)/L_6]^2 = \tfrac{6}{5}[\sigma_6(l)/L_6]^2 = 4.315 \times 10^{-8}.$$

Similarly, for the diameter measurements we have

$$[s_{12}(d)/D_{12}]^2 = \tfrac{12}{11}[\sigma_{12}(d)/D_{12}]^2 = 3.4055 \times 10^{-4}.$$

Then the overall relative precision of the method has for its best estimate, according to Equation 2.11,

$$s_{6\,12}(r)/R_{6\,12} = [4.315 \times 10^{-8} + 4 \times 3.4055 \times 10^{-4}]^{\frac{1}{2}}$$
$$= 3.691 \times 10^{-2}$$

or

$$s_{6\,12}(r) = 0.285 \text{ ohm}.$$

2.8.7 (See page 36)

These results can most easily be thought of in terms of the graph relating $z = f(x)$ and x (figure 2.2). Z is the true value of

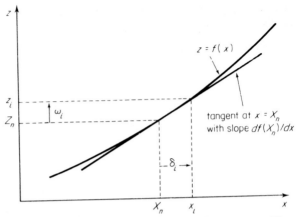

Figure 2.2

the function corresponding to the true value X of the measured quantity; ω_i is the deviation from the estimate Z_n corresponding to a measurement deviation δ_i from x_n.

If $f(z)$ differs very little from a straight line over the range of measured values of δ_i, the errors in z will simply be equal to those in x multiplied by a constant factor. This factor is the slope of the tangent at X_n, that is $df(X_n)/dx$. Only when this tangent ceases to be a good approximation to the curve over the measurement range will the results of section 2.3.6 become unreliable.

Example 7

A simple theodolite, set up at exactly 10 m from the wall of a building, is used to measure the vertical angle subtended by the building. Five measurements of this are 52.4°, 52.6°, 52.9°, 52.1° and 52.5°. What is the height of the building and how precise is the method of measurement?

If h is the height of the building in meters, and θ is the measured angle,

$$h = 10 \tan \theta.$$

The best estimate of θ is the mean of the measured values

$$\Theta_5 = 52.5°$$

and the deviations are $-0.1°$, $0.1°$, $0.4°$, $-0.4°$ and $0°$, with root mean square value

$$\sigma_5(\theta) = 0.2608° = \pi \times 0.26/180 = 4.552 \times 10^{-3} \text{ radian.}$$
$$dh/d\theta = 10 \sec^2 \theta = 26.985 \text{ m}$$

at $\theta = \Theta_5 = 52.5°$.

Hence the best estimate of the height is, from Equation 2.13,

$$H_5 = 10 \tan \Theta_5 = 10 \tan 52.5° = 13.032 \text{ m.}$$

The root mean square deviation is, from Equation 2.14,

$$\sigma_5(h) = \sigma_5(\theta) \, dh(52.5°)/d\theta$$
$$= \sigma_5(\theta) \times 10 \sec^2 (52.5°)$$
$$= 4.552 \times 26.985 \times 10^{-3} = 0.1228 \text{ m.}$$

Hence the best estimate of precision is

$$s_5(h) = (5/4)^{\frac{1}{2}} \sigma_5(h) = 0.1373 \text{ m.}$$

To see whether the method of calculation proposed in section 2.3.6 is reliable we note that the estimates of height corresponding to the extreme measurements $\theta_3 = 52.9°$ and $\theta_4 = 52.1°$, assuming the relationship between height and angle is linear over this range, are

$$h_3 = 13.032 + \pi \times 0.4 \times 10 \sec^2 (52.5°)/180 = 13.220 \text{ m,}$$
$$h_4 = 13.032 - \pi \times 0.4 \times 10 \sec^2 (52.5°)/180 = 12.844 \text{ m.}$$

The actual heights corresponding to these angles would be

$$h'_3 = 10 \tan 52.9° = 13.222 \text{ m,}$$
$$h'_4 = 10 \tan 52.1° = 12.846 \text{ m.}$$

The differences $h'_3 - h_3$ and $h'_4 - h_4$ are very small compared with $\sigma_5(h)$ which gives a typical value of the deviations in h, so we conclude that the method is satisfactory.

    The situation would have been very different had the five measurements been $88.9°$, $89.1°$, $89.4°$, $88.6°$, $89.0°$, which have a mean

$$\Theta_5 = 89.0°$$

and the same root mean square deviation

$$\sigma_5(\theta) = 0.2608°.$$

Applying the same formulae as above we obtain

$$H_5 = 572.9 \text{ m (rather a tall building!)}$$
$$\sigma_5(h) = 149.5 \text{ m.}$$

However, corresponding to the measured angles the heights should be

$$h'_1 = 10 \tan 88.9° = 520.8, \qquad h'_2 = 636.6, \qquad h'_3 = 954.9,$$
$$h'_4 = 409.2, \qquad h'_5 = 572.9 \text{ m.}$$

These have mean value

$$H'_5 = 618.9 \text{ m}$$

and root mean square deviation

$$\sigma'_5(h) = 285.8 \text{ m,}$$

which differ markedly from the earlier estimates. We can see why this should be so by plotting $h = 10 \tan \theta$ in the region of $\theta = 89.0°$ as shown in figure 2.3. It is clear that the errors involved in using the tangent at $\theta = 89.0°$ for the true curve relating h and θ are comparable with those arising from the measurement errors in θ.

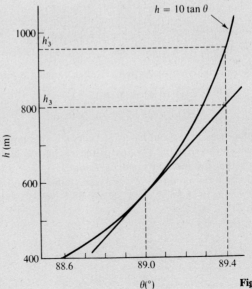

Figure 2.3

2.8.8   Example 8 (See page 42)

Determine the height of the building of Example 4 (page 48) and its standard error.

We have already calculated

$$X_{16} = 33.488 \text{ m}, \qquad s_{16} = 0.017 \text{ m}.$$

Hence, from section 2.4, the standard error is

$$S_{16} = s_{16}/16^{\frac{1}{2}} = 0.00425 \text{ m}$$

and we may express the height as

$$(33.488 \pm 0.00425) \text{ m}.$$

However, section 2.5 shows that the proportional error in S_{16} is

$$\sigma(S_{16})/S_{16} \sim 1/14^{\frac{1}{2}} \sim 0.27$$

or

$$\sigma(S_{16}) \sim 0.001 \text{ m}.$$

The number of measurements, therefore, does not warrant more than one significant place in the standard error, and the result would more justifiably be expressed as (33.488 ± 0.005) m.

2.8.9   Example 9 (See page 43)

What is the standard error of the total mass determined in Example 5 (page 49)?

The standard error of the iron volume is given by

$$S_8^2(x) = \sigma_8^2(x)/7 = 0.00357 \text{ cm}^6$$

and that for the aluminium is

$$S_{15}^2(y) = \sigma_{15}^2(y)/14 = 0.00414 \text{ cm}^6.$$

Since the mass, z, is related to the volumes x and y by

$$z = 7.88x + 2.70y,$$

then, from section 2.6.1, the standard error in the mass is given by

$$\begin{aligned} S_{8\ 15}(z) &= [7.88^2 S_8^2(x) + 2.70^2 S_{15}^2(y)]^{\frac{1}{2}} \\ &= 0.502 \text{ g}. \end{aligned}$$

Now

$$S_8(x) = 0.0598 \text{ cm}^3,$$

but since this is derived from only eight measurements, section 2.5 shows that

$$S_8(x) = 0.06 \text{ cm}^3$$

is an adequate result. Similarly

$$S_{15}(y) = 0.0644 \text{ cm}^3$$

is better given as

$$S_{15}(y) = 0.07 \text{ cm}^3.$$

Neither of the individual standard errors can justifiably be given to more than one significant figure and this will remain true of the overall error to which they contribute. Hence

$$S_{8\,15}(z) = 0.5 \text{ g}$$

and the mass can be written as (232.5 ± 0.5) g.

2.8.10   Example 10 (See page 43)

What is the standard error of the resistance determined in Example 6?

The standard error of the length, l, of the wire is given by

$$S_6^2(l) = \sigma_6^2(l)/5 = 0.002 \text{ cm}^2$$

and the best estimate of its length is

$$L_6 = 527.3 \text{ cm}.$$

Similarly for the diameter, d,

$$S_{12}^2(d) = \sigma_{12}^2(d)/11 = 1.09 \times 10^{-7} \text{ cm}^3$$

and

$$D_{12} = 0.062 \text{ cm}.$$

Since the resistance, r, is related to the length and diameter by

$$r = 56.28 \times 10^{-6} l d^{-2},$$

then, from section 2.6.2, the relative standard error in the resistance is given by

$$S_{6\,12}(r)/R_{6\,12} = [S_6^2(l)/L_6^2 + 4S_{12}^2(d)/D_{12}^2]^{\frac{1}{2}}$$
$$= 0.0107$$

or

$$S_{6\,12}(r) = 0.0826 \text{ ohm}.$$

In this example, too, the comparatively small number of measurements does not warrant expressing either the individual or total errors to more than one significant figure. Hence

$$S_{6\,12}(r) = 0.09 \text{ ohm}$$

and the resistance of the wire may be written as (7.72 ± 0.09) ohm.

2.8.11 (See page 44)

In the previous example the partial derivatives are

$$\partial r/\partial l = (4\rho/\pi)\, d^{-2}, \qquad \partial r/\partial d = -(8\rho/\pi)ld^{-3}.$$

Thus if rough measurements had given

$$l = 530 \text{ cm}, \qquad d = 0.06 \text{ cm}$$

the derivatives at these values would have been

$$\partial r/\partial l = 1.56 \times 10^{-2}, \qquad \partial r/\partial d = -2.76 \times 10^2.$$

This is sufficient to show that the standard error for d should be about 10^4 smaller than that for l if their contributions to the error in r are to be matched. Thus with the given values

$$\sigma_{12}(d) = 1.095 \times 10^{-3} \text{ cm}, \qquad S_{12}(d) = 3.30 \times 10^{-4} \text{ cm}$$

there is little point in aiming at a standard error for l much better than 1 cm. Suppose we had been content with only two measurements of l giving

$$L_2 = 527 \text{ cm}, \qquad \sigma_2(l) = 1 \text{ cm}.$$

These, together with

$$D_{12} = 0.062 \text{ cm}, \qquad \sigma_{12}(d) = 1.095 \times 10^{-3} \text{ cm}$$

would have given

$$R_{2\,12} = 7.715 \text{ ohm},$$
$$S_{2\,12} = [5.35 \times 10^{-5} + 6.757 \times 10^{-3}]^{\frac{1}{2}}$$
$$= 8.25 \times 10^{-2} \text{ ohm}.$$

Thus the much less accurate determination of l has not altered the results above significantly. As the errors in d still predominate it is clear that a method of measurement of greater precision is required for it if r is to be derived with greater accuracy.

2.9 PROBLEMS

7. What are the best estimates of the standard deviations and of the standard errors for each of the series of measurements A, B, C, in Problem 1 (page 23)? How would you present the results in each case? Do you consider them consistent?

8. Here are 100 measurements (in cm) of the same length (X):

```
21  19  24  26  23  24  25  27  22  23
25  20  24  29  21  27  26  25  22  25
28  24  26  25  20  23  21  23  24  25
24  26  21  22  19  24  28  25  26  23
25  20  22  26  27  21  25  23  27  26
21  22  27  26  25  28  24  23  25  24
29  24  24  21  27  25  22  25  25  21
20  21  25  23  23  26  24  24  23  27
23  20  25  23  24  27  23  22  20  24
21  26  28  23  23  22  26  25  21  26
```

a) Divide these into ten groups of ten (by taking each row, for example) and calculate for each group the mean (X_{10}), the adjusted r.m.s. deviation (s_{10}) and the adjusted error (S_{10}). Compare these ten estimates of the standard error with the value you obtain by finding the adjusted standard deviation of the ten values of the means (X_{10}).

b) repeat these calculations with ten different groups of ten (by taking each column, for example).

9. Use each of the two histograms of Problem 2 (page 23) to give a value for the volume and its error. Do the two results differ significantly?

10. Two methods were used to measure the breaking force for a sample of steel wire. The first ten measurements from each were:

	Breaking force (tons weight)								
A	3.3	3.5	3.7	3.2	3.6	3.5	3.6	3.4	3.6	3.9
B	3.5	3.6	3.6	3.7	3.5	3.6	3.5	3.5	3.6	3.5

What estimate of precision would you make for each method? How many measurements would you expect to have to make, using the less precise method, in order to give a result as accurate as the ten given measurements from the more precise one?

11. An experiment to measure length has a standard error independent of

the length. Three points A, B, C, are in a straight line. AB is measured (i) directly, (ii) by measuring AC and BC and taking their difference. What is the ratio of the standard errors with which AB is determined in the two cases?

12. An electric probe can slide along a longitudinal slot in a waveguide and thereby measure the electric field strength of the electromagnetic field in the guide. Nodes (points of zero field) occur at each half-wavelength and for a certain frequency of the field were recorded at the following positions (in cm): 6.42, 8.37, 10.21, 12.14, 14.10, 15.95, 17.88, 19.76, 21.74, 23.61.

Student A calculates each interval between consecutive nodes by subtracting each measurement from the next, thus obtaining nine measurements of the half-wavelength ($\lambda/2$). Student B subtracts the first measurement from the second, the third from the fourth and so on, thus obtaining five measurements of $\lambda/2$. Student C subtracts the first measurement from the sixth, the second from the seventh and so on, thus obtaining five measurements of $5\lambda/2$. Each student then takes the mean of his wavelength measurements for his best estimate.

a) What are the three values?

b) Show that A's method wastes all the observations except the first and last.

c) Show that C's method gives an accuracy five times better than B's.

13. A land speed test is conducted over a track of length 1.0000 ± 0.0001 miles. The time for its traversal is 11.532 ± 0.005 sec. What is the speed of the car? If you wished to improve the accuracy would you concentrate first on the timing apparatus or the measurement of the mile? How far could you improve it without attending to both?

14. Two resistors have resistances 10.7 ± 0.2 ohm and 26.5 ± 0.5 ohm. What is their resistance when connected (i) in series, (ii) in parallel?

15. A fast singly charged nuclear particle travels through a magnetic field perpendicular to its motion. The sagitta, d, of a chord between points $2l$ apart on the circular path gives the particle's energy, V electron volts, according to the formula

$$V = \frac{H^2 l^4}{45.43 d^2}$$

if H is measured in gauss and l and d in cm. If H, l and d are measured with a standard error of 1% how accurately is V known? What improvement is achieved if the error in l is reduced to 0.1%

16. One student, following the results of section 2.3.3, says that if $z = 4x$, then $\sigma(z) = 4\sigma(x)$. Another student says that, since $z = x + x + x + x$, the same section shows that $\sigma(z) = 2\sigma(x)$. How does this apparent discrepancy arise and which argument is fallacious?

CHAPTER 3

Least squares

In the first two chapters we have seen how to calculate numbers that describe an experiment in a useful way. The formulae are rather like some cooks' recipes—what you have to do is clear enough but any precise reasons remain rather a mystery. What we did was to appeal to common sense in order to get started, and this involved some apparently arbitrary decisions about what we would mean precisely by terms such as 'true' and 'best' which we commonly use in everyday language.

We shall see later, after we have examined the ways in which measurement variations arise, that these decisions have a much greater significance than merely arbitrary choices. However, even at this stage it is possible to link what we have done by an underlying principle that can be used to answer some questions that still remain. This is the principle of *least squares*.

3.1 MEAN AS BEST ESTIMATE OF TRUE VALUE

The simplest demonstration of the principle is as follows. Suppose measurements $x_1, x_2, \ldots, x_n$ are made of a quantity whose true value is X. Then the measurements have errors $\varepsilon_1 = x_1 - X$, $\varepsilon_2 = x_2 - X, \ldots, \varepsilon_n = x_n - X$, and the sum of their squares is

$$E = \varepsilon_1^2 + \varepsilon_2^2 + \ldots + \varepsilon_n^2 = (x_1 - X)^2 + (x_2 - X)^2 + \ldots + (x_n - X)^2.$$

X, of course, is an unknown quantity which the experiment sets out to find. E, the sum of the squared errors, varies as X varies. The principle of least squares states that *the best choice for X is the one that makes E a minimum*. At the minimum, $X = X_0$ say,

$$\partial E/\partial X = -2(x_1 - X) - 2(x_2 - X) - \ldots - 2(x_n - X)$$
$$= 0.$$

Hence

$$X_0 = (x_1 + x_2 + \ldots + x_n)/n,$$

and this agrees with our earlier choice of X_n, the mean, as the best estimate for X, the true value.

3.2   SUM OF TWO QUANTITIES $(z = x + y)$

As a second example let us consider, as in section 2.3.2, the sum of any pair of values, x_i from the n measurements of x, and y_j from the m measurements of y. This will have an error relative to the true value, Z, of amount

$$\varepsilon_{ij} = x_i + y_j - Z.$$

The sum of the squared errors is

$$E = \sum_{i=1}^{n} \sum_{j=1}^{m} \varepsilon_{ij}^2 = \sum_{i=1}^{n} \sum_{j=1}^{m} (x_i + y_j - Z)^2.$$

E is a minimum for variations in Z when

$$\partial E/\partial Z = -2 \sum_{i=1}^{n} \sum_{j=1}^{m} (x_i + y_j - Z)$$

$$= -2 \sum_{i=1}^{n} (mx_i + mY_m - mZ)$$

$$= -2(mnX_n + mnY_m - mnZ)$$

$$= 0,$$

which occurs for the value $Z = Z_0$, where

$$Z_0 = X_n + Y_m.$$

So the principle of least squares again gives the same result as before. This is true for any of the cases treated in Chapter 2.

3.3   BEST STRAIGHT LINE: LINEAR REGRESSION

Quite often a physical quantity that can be expressed by a single number varies with the conditions under which it is measured, and our experiment sets out to find this relationship. The simplest of these is the linear type of relationship. For example the length, l, of a metal rod depends linearly upon its temperature, T:

$$l = l_0(1 + \alpha T),$$

where l_0 is the length of the rod at $T = 0$ and α is its coefficient of linear expansion. The inverse of the current, i, delivered by a battery depends linearly upon the resistance, r, connected across it:

$$1/i = (r + R)/V_E,$$

where V_E is the electromotive force of the battery and R is its internal resistance.

All such cases can be expressed in the form

$$y = ax + b,$$

where x and y are the two quantities which are measured—T and l in the first example, and r and $1/i$ in the second—and a and b are, or are related to, the quantities the experiment is designed to determine—αl_0 and l_0 in the first case, and $1/V_E$ and R/V_E in the second.

We could find a and b by choosing two pairs of measured values x_1, y_1 and x_2, y_2 and solving the two simultaneous equations,

$$y_1 = ax_1 + b,$$
$$y_2 = ax_2 + b$$

for the unknowns a and b.

For example, in the electrical experiment a resistance r_1 would give a current i_1, and a second resistance r_2 would give the current i_2. If each were measured only once we should have a single determination of V_E and of R, with no possibility of estimating precision or error. Repeated measurements of the *same* two resistances and the *same* two currents would enable us first to calculate standard errors for them and from these the standard error in V_E and R.

However, it may be inconvenient to keep constant the quantities that are to be repeatedly measured. If, in the first example, we wished to measure the rod many times at the same temperature a thermostatically controlled enclosure would be necessary. It is preferable in such cases to measure a whole set of different values $x_1, x_2, \ldots, x_n$, together with their corresponding values $y_1, y_2, \ldots, y_n$. Thus the metal rod could be allowed to vary in temperature, or made to do so, and we would measure its temperature at the same time as its length.

If all the measurements were without error and the linear relationship were true, then all the points (x_1, y_1), (x_2, y_2), ..., (x_n, y_n) plotted as a Cartesian graph would lie exactly on a straight line. Its slope, dy/dx, would give the unknown a and its intercept on the y axis would give the second unknown b. However, one and perhaps both the measured quantities will be subject to error and the plotted points will therefore lie about the true straight line, close to it if the errors are small, more widely scattered if the errors are large. The problem now is to give the best estimate of this true straight line—to decide what is the 'best' line.

The least squares principle can quite easily be used here. In its simplest form we assume that the precision with which x is measured is much greater than for y. This is equivalent to saying that we can plot the x-value of each point without error, and that *if* we knew a and b, the true value of y could then be plotted as $ax + b$. Corresponding to the values $x_1, x_2, \ldots, x_n$ would be the true values $y_1^*, y_2^*, \ldots, y_n^*$ and all the points $(x_1, y_1^*), (x_2, y_2^*), \ldots, (x_n, y_n^*)$ would lie on the true straight line. The errors in the measured values of y at these points would then be

$$\varepsilon_1 = y_1 - y_1^* = y_1 - ax_1 - b,$$

$$\varepsilon_2 = y_2 - y_2^* = y_2 - ax_2 - b,$$

$$\cdot \qquad \cdot \qquad \cdot$$

$$\varepsilon_n = y_n - y_n^* = y_n - ax_n - b,$$

as shown in figure 3.1.

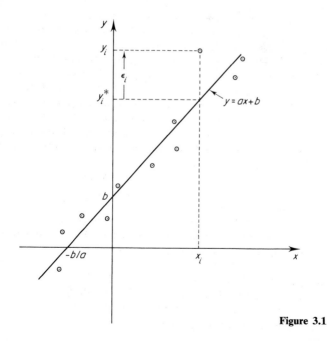

Figure 3.1

The sum of squares to be minimized is the sum of these squared errors,

$$E = \varepsilon_1^2 + \varepsilon_2^2 + \ldots + \varepsilon_n^2$$
$$= (y_1 - ax_1 - b)^2 + (y_2 - ax_2 - b)^2 + \ldots$$
$$+ (y_n - ax_n - b)^2. \tag{3.1}$$

In section 3.1 E depended only upon X, the assumed true value, and the minimum occurred for $\partial E/\partial X = 0$. Here, where E depends upon two assumed true values (for a and for b), its partial derivative with respect to each must be zero at its minimum,

$$\partial E/\partial a = 0 \quad \text{and} \quad \partial E/\partial b = 0.$$

These equations simplify to

$$(XY)_n - a(X^2)_n - bX_n = 0, \tag{3.2}$$
$$Y_n - aX_n - b = 0, \tag{3.3}$$

where

$$X_n = (x_1 + x_2 + \ldots + x_n)/n,$$
$$Y_n = (y_1 + y_2 + \ldots + y_n)/n,$$
$$(X^2)_n = (x_1^2 + x_2^2 + \ldots + x_n^2)/n,$$
$$(XY)_n = (x_1 y_1 + x_2 y_2 + \ldots + x_n y_n)/n.$$

Note that X_n and Y_n, although they have a mathematical form similar to that for our earlier use of these symbols for average values, have here a different physical significance. Previously they were used as average values of repeated measurements of the *same* quantity; here they are averages of the measurements of a set of numerically different quantities. In mechanical terms (X_n, Y_n) would be the 'centre of mass' or centroid of n equal masses placed at the points (x_1, y_1), (x_2, y_2), ..., (x_n, y_n). Equation 3.3 shows that the best straight line passes through this centroid. Solving Equations 3.2 and 3.3 we have for the best estimates of a and b,

$$a_n = [(XY)_n - X_n Y_n]/[(X^2)_n - X_n^2], \tag{3.4}$$
$$b_n = [(X^2)_n Y_n - X_n (XY)_n]/[(X^2)_n - X_n^2]. \tag{3.5}$$

The errors in a_n and b_n arise only from errors in $y_1, y_2, \ldots, y_n$ since $x_1, x_2, \ldots, x_n$ and consequently X_n and $(X^2)_n$ are assumed to have negligible errors. From Equation 3.4

$$a_n = [(x_1 - X_n)y_1 + (x_2 - X_n)y_2 + \ldots$$
$$+ (x_n - X_n)y_n]/\{n[(X^2)_n - X_n^2]\}.$$

Hence its standard deviation is, according to section 2.3.3,

$$\sigma(a_n) = \frac{[(x_1 - X_n)^2\sigma^2(y_1) + (x_2 - X_n)^2\sigma^2(y_2) + \ldots + (x_n - X_n)^2\sigma^2(y_n)]^{\frac{1}{2}}}{n[(X^2)_n - X_n^2]}.$$

We now have to make some decision about the standard deviations of the y values. We have, in effect, already made an important decision about these. In the preceding equations all the y values occur symmetrically, or with equal importance, and this can be traced back to the expression for E (Equations 3.1) where the squared error of each y occurs with unit coefficient. This means that all the errors have equal importance. Now each value is measured only once so their equal importance is equivalent to saying that the precision of each measurement is the same. Hence

$$\sigma(y_1) = \sigma(y_2) = \ldots = \sigma(y_n)$$
$$= \sigma(y),$$

say. Then

$$\sigma(a_n) = [(x_1 - X_n)^2 + (x_2 - X_n)^2 + \ldots + (x_n - X_n)^2]^{\frac{1}{2}}\sigma(y)/$$
$$\{n[(X^2)_n - X_n^2]\}$$
$$= [x_1^2 + \ldots + x_n^2 - 2X_n(x_1 + \ldots + x_n) + nX_n^2]^{\frac{1}{2}}\sigma(y)/$$
$$\{n[(X^2)_n - X_n^2]\}$$
$$= \sigma(y)/\{n[(X^2)_n - X_n^2]\}^{\frac{1}{2}}.$$

Similarly, by rewriting Equation 3.5 as

$$b_n = \frac{[(X^2)_n - X_n x_1]y_1 + [(X^2)_n - X_n x_2]y_2 + \ldots + [(X^2)_n - X_n x_n]y_n}{n[(X^2)_n - X_n^2]}.$$

we find that

$$\sigma(b_n) = \sigma(y)(X^2)_n^{\frac{1}{2}}/\{n[(X^2)_n - X_n^2]\}^{\frac{1}{2}}.$$

Once a_n and b_n have been calculated from Equations 3.4 and 3.5 we can calculate the n deviations

$$\delta_1 = y_1 - a_n x_1 - b_n,$$
$$\delta_2 = y_2 - a_n x_2 - b_n,$$
$$\cdot \qquad \cdot$$
$$\cdot \qquad \cdot$$
$$\delta_n = y_n - a_n x_n - b_n,$$

and use these to give $s_n(y)$, the best estimate of $\sigma(y)$.

In section 2.2 we saw that σ_n could *not* be the best estimate of σ because it was clearly wrong when $n = 1$. Here we cannot obtain a meaningful estimate of $\sigma(y)$ even for two measurements, for we can always put a straight line through two points, and this would necessarily be the best line if this was all the experimental evidence available. The two deviations from this line, δ_1 and δ_2, would both be zero in this case, while estimates of the accuracy of the parameters, a and b, defining the line would be impossible. The best estimate, as we therefore might expect, turns out to be

$$s_n(y) = (\delta_1^2 + \delta_2^2 + \ldots + \delta_n^2)^{\frac{1}{2}}/(n-2)^{\frac{1}{2}}$$
$$= \sigma_n(y)n^{\frac{1}{2}}/(n-2)^{\frac{1}{2}}.$$

Since we make only the one determination of a and of b, their standard errors will be the same as their standard deviations, and the best estimates of these will be

$$S_n(a) = \sigma_n(y)/\{(n-2)[(X^2)_n - X_n^2]\}^{\frac{1}{2}}, \qquad (3.6)$$
$$S_n(b) = \sigma_n(y)(X^2)_n^{\frac{1}{2}}/\{(n-2)[(X^2)_n - X_n^2]\}^{\frac{1}{2}}. \qquad (3.7)$$

Using Equation 3.3 with a and b given their best estimated values, a typical deviation can be written as

$$\delta_i = y_i - a_n x_i - b_n$$
$$= y_i - Y_n - a_n(x_i - X_n).$$

Hence

$$\sum_{i=1}^{n} \delta_i^2 = \sum_{i=1}^{n} (y_i - Y_n)^2 - 2a_n \sum_{i=1}^{n} (y_i - Y_n)(x_i - X_n)$$
$$+ a_n^2 \sum_{i=1}^{n} (x_i - X_n)^2$$
$$= n(Y^2)_n - nY_n^2 - 2na_n[(XY)_n - X_n Y_n]$$
$$+ na_n^2[(X^2)_n - X_n^2]$$

which, using Equation 3.4, gives the mean square deviation of y in the form

$$\sigma_n^2(y) = \sum_{i=1}^{n} \delta_i^2/n = (Y^2)_n - Y_n^2 - [(XY)_n - X_n Y_n]^2/[(X^2)_n - X_n^2].$$

$$(3.8)$$

For calculations it is often simpler to rewrite Equations 3.4 to 3.8 in a form that avoids the mean values

$$X_n = (x_1 + x_2 + \ldots + x_n)/n, \quad \text{etc.},$$

and uses instead the summations that we denote by

$$\Sigma x = \sum_{i=1}^{n} x_i = nX_n = x_1 + x_2 + \ldots + x_n, \quad \text{etc.}$$

The equations then become

$$a_n = [n\Sigma xy - \Sigma x\Sigma y]/[n\Sigma x^2 - (\Sigma x)^2], \tag{3.9}$$

$$b_n = [\Sigma x^2\Sigma y - \Sigma x\Sigma xy]/[n\Sigma x^2 - (\Sigma x)^2], \tag{3.10}$$

$$S_n(a) = n\sigma_n(y)/\{(n-2)[n\Sigma x^2 - (\Sigma x)^2]\}^{\frac{1}{2}}, \tag{3.11}$$

$$S_n(b) = n\sigma_n(y)(\Sigma x^2)^{\frac{1}{2}}/\{n(n-2)[n\Sigma x^2 - (\Sigma x)^2]\}^{\frac{1}{2}}, \tag{3.12}$$

$$n^2\sigma_n^2(y) = n\Sigma y^2 - (\Sigma y)^2 - [n\Sigma xy - \Sigma x\Sigma y]^2/[n\Sigma x^2 - (\Sigma x)^2]. \tag{3.13}$$

[See §3.7.1,
page 77;
§3.7.2,
page 80;
§3.7.3,
page 80;
§3.7.4,
page 81]

The least squares method of estimating the best straight line is often referred to as *linear regression*. When, as above, the x values are assumed precise this line is called the *line of regression of y on x*; when the values of y are taken to be precise it is the *line of regression of x on y*.

3.4 CORRELATION

In the type of problem dealt with in section 3.3 we knew, or assumed, that a relationship did exist between the two variables, or sets of measurements such as i and r, and that the purpose of the analysis was to find the best estimates of the parameters such as R and V_E that defined the relationship. However, a most important part of experimental research concerns the question of whether the observations provide good evidence for assuming that there is a relationship at all between two measured quantities. This Section shows how we might answer that question.

We noted that Equation 3.3 showed the best line to be one passing through the 'centroid' (X_n, Y_n), where X_n and Y_n are the mean values of the measurements. If, therefore, we shift the Cartesian axes to have their origin at this centroid the best straight line will pass through the new origin, and we shall then be concerned only with its slope.

After plotting the measurements using the new axes we shall then have a set of points spread in some way, roughly equally, about the origin. At one extreme we may find the points closely following a straight line as in figures 3.2 and 3.3. At the other the

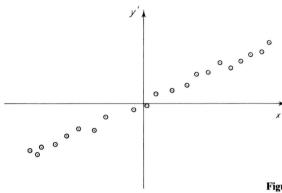

Figure 3.2

points may be widely scattered, following no clear pattern, as in figure 3.4. Examination of the former suggests two criteria for supporting the existence of a linear relationship:

1. The slope of the line regression of y on x should agree with that of the line of regression of x on y.

2. The standard errors of the slopes of these lines should be small.

To simplify the algebra we shall use, instead of the actual measurements x_i and y_i, their values calculated from the mean,

$$x_i' = x_i - X_n, \qquad y_i' = y_i - Y_n.$$

(These are, of course, the quantities plotted in figures 3.2, 3.3 and

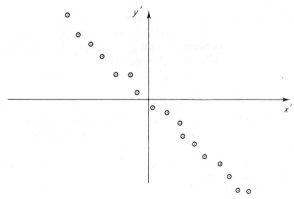

Figure 3.3

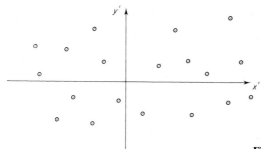

Figure 3.4

3.4.) Then

$$\Sigma x' = \Sigma y' = 0,$$

and the straight line, whose significance we are investigating, will be

$$y' = ax',$$

where the y' values are subject to error, but the x' values are assumed precise. Equation 3.13 shows that the mean square deviation of any y' measurement from its true value is now given by

$$n\sigma_n^2(y') = [\Sigma x'^2\Sigma y'^2 - (\Sigma x'y')^2]/\Sigma x'^2.$$

Hence, using Equations 3.9 and 3.11, the best estimate for a is

$$a_n = \Sigma x'y'/\Sigma x'^2 \qquad (3.14)$$

and its standard error is

$$S_n(a) = \frac{[\Sigma x'^2\Sigma y'^2 - (\Sigma x'y')^2]^{\frac{1}{2}}}{(n-2)^{\frac{1}{2}}\Sigma x'^2},$$

or

$$S_n(a) = \left[\frac{(1-r^2)\Sigma y'^2}{(n-2)\Sigma x'^2}\right]^{\frac{1}{2}} \qquad (3.15)$$

where

$$r = \Sigma x'y'/(\Sigma x'^2\Sigma y'^2)^{\frac{1}{2}} \qquad (3.16)$$

and is known as the *coefficient of correlation*.

Interchanging x' and y' enables us to deal with the line of regression of x' on y'. If we write this as

$$x' = a^*y',$$

the best estimate of a^* is then

$$a_n^* = \Sigma x'y'/\Sigma y'^2 \qquad (3.17)$$

with standard error

$$S_n(a^*) = \left[\frac{(1-r^2)\Sigma x'^2}{(n-2)\Sigma y'^2}\right]^{\frac{1}{2}}, \qquad (3.18)$$

Thus the criteria suggested above require the slopes given by Equations 3.14 and 3.17 to agree, and their errors given by Equations 3.15 and 3.18 to be small. We must already be aware that using words like 'agree' and 'small' nearly always involve some degree of human choice or preference, based upon experience or prejudice, which cannot be excluded entirely by mathematical analysis.

3.4.1 Perfect correlation

Nevertheless, there are idealized extreme cases where it would be perverse not to accept that 'agree' and 'small' have an unambiguous meaning. For example, suppose that in figure 3.2 or 3.3 the points lay *exactly* on a straight line. In this case the two lines of regression would be the same. Since the roles of x' and y' are interchanged for the two lines their slopes will be the reciprocal, each of the other,

$$a_n = 1/a_n^*, \qquad (3.19)$$

and, since no point deviates from the common straight line, the errors in the slopes will be zero,

$$S_n(a) = S_n(a^*) = 0. \qquad (3.20)$$

Equations 3.14 and 3.17 show that for Equation 3.19 to be true we must have

$$\Sigma x'y'/\Sigma x'^2 = \Sigma y'^2/\Sigma x'y'. \qquad (3.21)$$

Equations 3.15 and 3.18 show that Equations 3.20 will be satisfied when

$$(1-r^2)\Sigma y'^2/\Sigma x'^2 = (1-r^2)\Sigma x'^2/\Sigma y'^2 = 0. \qquad (3.22)$$

Assuming that

$$\Sigma x'^2 \neq 0 \quad \text{and} \quad \Sigma y'^2 \neq 0,$$

which are special cases to be dealt with below, we see, using
Equation 3.16, that the conditions 3.21 and 3.22 reduce to the
single one

$$r = \Sigma x'y'/(\Sigma x'^2 \Sigma y'^2)^{\frac{1}{2}} = \pm 1. \tag{3.23}$$

For these values of the coefficient of correlation we would
certainly be justified in saying that the slopes of the two lines
agreed (since they are than identical) and that their errors were
small (both of them zero). We therefore take the values 3.23 as
denoting perfect correlation between the quantities concerned.

3.4.2 No correlation

As an opposite extreme suppose the results in figure 3.3 were
scattered about so as to give for every measurement point at
(x'_i, y'_i) another at $(x'_i, -y'_i)$ or one at $(-x'_i, y'_i)$. Then

$$\Sigma x'_i y'_i = 0$$

so, provided again that

$$\Sigma x'^2_i \neq 0 \quad \text{and} \quad \Sigma y'^2_i \neq 0,$$

we will have

$$r = 0.$$

Then

$$a_n = 0, \qquad a_n^* = 0$$

and

$$S_n(a) = \left[\frac{\Sigma y'^2}{(n-2)\Sigma x'^2}\right]^{\frac{1}{2}}, \qquad S_n(a^*) = \left[\frac{\Sigma x'^2}{(n-2)\Sigma y'^2}\right]^{\frac{1}{2}}.$$

Thus the two lines of regression, which in this case are the x'
and y' axes, are as contradictory as possible (at right angles to each
other). This contradiction is reinforced when, because of the
$(n-2)^{-\frac{1}{2}}$ dependence of the errors, their slopes are apparently
determined with greater and greater accuracy as the number of
measurements is increased.

3.4.3 Degree of correlation

It may be shown that, since the x' and y' values are real, r^2 can
only take values between 0 and 1. We have seen above that it is
the extremes of this range that correspond with no correlation
($r = 0$) and perfect correlation ($|r| = 1$). We may also note, from

Equations 3.14, 3.16 and 3.17, that

$$a_n a_n^* = r^2 \qquad (3.24)$$

and, from Equations 3.15 and 3.18, that

$$S_n(a)/a_n = S_n(a^*)/a_n^* = [(1-r^2)/(n-2)r^2]^{\frac{1}{2}}. \qquad (3.25)$$

Thus agreements between the slopes of the lines of regression steadily improves as $|r|$ increases from 0 to 1, as does the relative accuracy in determining the slopes. This suggests that the greater the value of $|r|$ the greater the justification for believing that the two measured quantities are really linked or correlated—hence the name *coefficient of correlation* for r.

At what value of $|r|$ should our doubts change to confidence? We should be cautious over basing conviction solely upon statistical analysis. Once the evidence begins to look interesting (which, in practice, often involves some subjective judgement) the wise experimenter will seek to indentify the physical, chemical, biological or other factors that his or her experiment appears to have discovered. This may then suggest other experiments and further hypotheses in which these factors should also appear. A more general method of testing how well a set of measurements accords with the predictions of a hypothesis is outlined in Chapter 6.

If then, we use the coefficient of correlation to decide whether to carry on with more experimentation and analysis, rather than as 'proof' of an hypothesis, one useful guide to this is the relative error of the slopes of the lines of regression. Suppose, for example, that we required the error not to exceed one third the value of the slope itself,

$$S_n(a) < a_n/3.$$

Equation 3.25 shows that this is equivalent to

$$(1-r^2)/r^2 < (n-2)/9$$

or

$$|r| > 3/(n+7)^{\frac{1}{2}}. \qquad (3.26)$$

The minimum value of $|r|$ that satisfies this condition decreases, as we would expect, with the number of observations. Corresponding values are given in figure 3.5.

It was convenient to present the analysis above in terms of x' and y', and hand calculations are often less tedious and prone to mistakes when using deviations from the mean. However, as was pointed out at the end of section 3.3, this is not so when modern

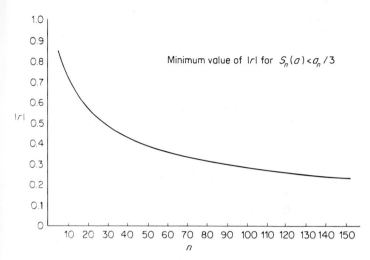

Figure 3.5

electronic calculators, which are often programmed to evaluate quantities such as Σx^2 and Σxy, are available. It is usually better then to calculate the correlation coefficient from the original measurements. It is simple to show that in terms of these quantities the expression 3.16 becomes

$$r = \frac{n\Sigma xy - \Sigma x \Sigma y}{[n\Sigma x^2 - (\Sigma x)^2]^{\frac{1}{2}}[n\Sigma y^2 - (\Sigma y)^2]^{\frac{1}{2}}}. \qquad (3.27)$$

When dealing with economic and social matters it is often fairly obvious, even before analysing the data, that two quantities are linked. For example, there is clearly *some* correlation between personal income and expenditure on holidays, since a person with very little income may be unable to afford any holiday while very expensive holidays could be enjoyed only by the rich. Consequently, if we were to plot holiday expenditure against income for a group of people we would undoubtedly find a line of regression of expenditure on income with a positive coefficient of correlation.

However, we would not, in this case, expect further work or analysis to isolate some social or economic factor, comparable with the physical one of resistance in section 3.3, which could predict with great accuracy how costly a person's holiday will be once his income is known. There will be rich people who prefer to stay at home, and poor people who use up their savings on a good holiday. The line of regression can still be very useful, nevertheless. Its slope predicts an average cost for persons with a particular income which can then be used to predict what the population as a whole, or within some income range, could be expected to spend on its holidays. The usefulness of such predictions depends greatly upon the accuracy with which the line of regression is determined. We have seen how this, in turn, depends upon the correlation coefficient.

3.4.4 Special cases

In sections 3.4.1 and 3.4.2 we excluded the cases

$$\Sigma y'^2 = 0, \qquad \Sigma x'^2 = 0.$$

The first implies that all the y' values are zero, so that all the points lie on the x'-axis. Since in this case

$$\Sigma x' y' = 0,$$

Equation 3.16 shows that the correlation coefficient has the indeterminate value $0/0$. Nevertheless, the line of regression of y' on x' is precisely determined—it is simply the straight line

$$y' = 0,$$

in accordance with equations 3.14 and 3.15, which give, in this case,

$$a_n = 0, \qquad S_n(a) = 0.$$

However, the fact that a straight line passes through all the points gives no support to any correlation between the x' and y' quantities. Clearly, within the range of the observations y' is quite independent of x'!

In practice we would be very unlikely to meet exactly this situation since, even if y' were truly constant throughout, there would be some measurement errors which would result in a positive value for $\Sigma y'^2$, though a small value for $|r|$ well below the limits of condition 3.26.

3.5 COMBINED EXPERIMENTS: LEAST ERROR

Although we were able, at the end of Chapter 2, to give a numerical comparison of Jenkins' and Robinson's results, this raised the further question of how their results might be combined to give an overall best estimate from the values (1.533 ± 0.007) sec and (1.514 ± 0.005) sec.

More generally, suppose $X_n \pm S_n$ is the result from one experiment and $X_m \pm S_m$ from another, where the *same* quantity is being measured in both cases. If S_n is very much smaller than S_m, which means that the first experiment is much more accurate than the second, we would believe the former and take X_n as the best estimate of the true value X. When S_m is very much smaller than S_n we would use X_m instead. If the two standard errors are equal we might think it very reasonable to take the mean.

$$X_{n,m} = \tfrac{1}{2}(X_n + X_m)$$

as the best estimate of the true value, since this accords equal importance to two experimental values of equal accuracy.

The simplest way of combining the results in the general case is to define

$$X_{n,m} = \alpha X_n + (1-\alpha)X_m, \qquad (3.28)$$

where

$$0 \le \alpha \le 1.$$

The coefficient α is determined by the relative errors of X_n and X_m. When X_n predominates because S_n/S_m is small, then α will be near unity and when X_m predominates because S_m/S_n is small, α will be near zero. Limiting α between these values ensures that $X_{n,m}$ lies between the values X_n and X_m.

We shall once more use the least squares principle to decide what expression we shall use for α. First, however, we shall restate the principle in a slightly different way. When in section 3.1 we minimized the sum of squares

$$E = \varepsilon_1^2 + \varepsilon_2^2 + \ldots + \varepsilon_n^2,$$

this also gave a minimum for the quantity

$$\sigma^2 = E/n = (\varepsilon_1^2 + \varepsilon_2^2 + \ldots + \varepsilon_n^2)/n$$

and for

$$S^2 = E/[n(n-1)] = (\varepsilon_1^2 + \varepsilon_2^2 + \ldots + \varepsilon_n^2)/[n(n-1)].$$

So S has its least value S_n—the standard error—when the value of X from which the errors are measured is the mean X_n and the ε_i therefore become the deviations δ_i from that mean.

Thus the principle of least squares can be restated as the *principle of least error*. Now from Equation 3.14 and the results of section 2.6.1, the standard error for the combined experiments is given by

$$S_{n,m}^2 = \sigma^2(X_{n,m}) = \alpha^2\sigma^2(X_n) + (1-\alpha)^2\sigma^2(X_m)$$
$$= \alpha^2 S_n^2 + (1-\alpha)^2 S_m^2.$$

This has a minimum when

$$d(S_{n,m}^2)/d\alpha = 0$$

or

$$\alpha S_n^2 - (1-\alpha)S_m^2 = 0.$$

Then

$$\alpha = \frac{S_n^{-2}}{S_n^{-2} + S_m^{-2}}, \qquad 1-\alpha = \frac{S_m^{-2}}{S_n^{-2} + S_m^{-2}}.$$

So the principle of least error gives for the best estimate of the combined result

$$X_{n,m} = \frac{1}{S_n^{-2} + S_m^{-2}}\left(\frac{X_n}{S_m^2} + \frac{X_m}{S_m^2}\right)$$

and its standard error is given by

$$S_{n,m}^2 = \frac{(S_n^{-2} + S_m^{-2})}{(S_n^{-2} + S_m^{-2})^2} = \frac{S_n^2 S_m^2}{S_m^2 + S_n^2},$$

or

$$S_{n,m}^{-2} = S_n^{-2} + S_m^{-2}.$$

We see that the estimates X_n, X_m are given an importance, or *weight*, proportional to $1/S_n^2$, $1/S_m^2$ respectively. For the general case where measurements $X_n \pm S_n$, $X_m \pm S_m$, $X_l \pm S_l, \ldots$ are to be combined, the weights which give least overall error are proportional to $1/S_n^2$, $1/S_m^2$, $1/S_l^2, \ldots$ so that the best combined estimate of the true value is the *weighted* mean,

$$X_{n,m,l,\ldots} = \frac{1}{S_n^{-2} + S_m^{-2} + S_l^{-2} + \ldots}\left(\frac{X_n}{S_n^2} + \frac{X_m}{S_m^2} + \frac{X_l}{S_l^2} + \ldots\right) \quad (3.29)$$

and its standard error is given by

[See §3.7.5, page 81]

$$S_{n,m,l,\ldots}^{-2} = S_n^{-2} + S_m^{-2} + S_l^{-2} + \ldots \quad (3.30)$$

3.6 COMBINED JENKINS AND ROBINSON EXPERIMENT

Now we can give a more complete assessment of the Jenkins and Robinson experiment:

1. After one measurement each we cannot combine the two results since we have no information about the errors. Any assessment of the relative reliability can only come from some source other than the results presented.

2. After five measurements each

$$X_n = 1.56 \text{ sec}, \qquad S_n = 0.07 \text{ sec},$$
$$X_m = 1.514 \text{ sec}, \qquad S_m = 0.005 \text{ sec}.$$

Hence, from Section 3.5,

$$X_{n,m} = 1.514 \text{ sec}, \qquad S_{n,m} = 0.005 \text{ sec}.$$

Note that since S_n is more than ten times as large as S_m and the weights go as the inverse *squares* of these errors, the best estimate of the true value and its standard error are, to the accuracy that the results warrant, determined entirely by Robinson's experiment (the more accurate one). Indeed, any experiments which have errors more than three or four times as great as others with which they are to be combined, have little influence on the final result and can usually be neglected.

3. The final results of Jenkins and Robinson are:

$$X_n = 1.533 \text{ sec}, \qquad S_n = 0.007 \text{ sec},$$
$$X_m = 1.514 \text{ sec}, \qquad S_m = 0.005 \text{ sec},$$

which combine, according to section 3.5, to give

$$X_{n,m} = 1.520 \text{ sec}, \qquad S_{n,m} = 0.004 \text{ sec}$$

or overall,

$$X = (1.520 \pm 0.004) \text{ sec}.$$

3.7 COMMENTS AND WORKED EXAMPLES

3.7.1 Example 11 (See page 67)

A vibrating tuning fork is used to mark at equal intervals of time a paper tape supposedly moving past it at uniform velocity. If the marks occur at distances 26.23, 37.72, 48.32, 58.96, 69.40, 80.85 and 91.68 cm from a fixed point of the tape and the frequency of the fork is known to be 256.0 sec^{-1}, what is the velocity of the tape?

If y is distance along the tape and t is the time, we may expect them to be related by

$$y = vt + y_0,$$

where v is the velocity. Since the experiment measures t in units of τ, the period of the fork, it is more convenient to use the variable

$$x = t/\tau$$

so that

$$y = v\tau x + y_0.$$

Hence a plot of y against x should be linear, with slope

$$a = v\tau.$$

From the results given we construct the following table:

$x = t/\tau$	y (cm)	x^2	xy (cm)	y^2 (cm^2)
0	26.23	0	0	688.01
1	37.72	1	37.72	1 422.80
2	48.32	4	96.64	2 334.82
3	58.96	9	176.88	3 476.28
4	69.40	16	277.60	4 816.36
5	80.85	25	404.25	6 536.72
6	91.68	36	550.08	8 405.22
21	413.16	91	1 543.17	27 680.21
Σx	Σy	Σx^2	Σxy	Σy^2

$$7\Sigma x^2 - (\Sigma x)^2 = 196$$

$$7\Sigma xy - \Sigma x \Sigma y = 2\,125.83 \text{ cm}$$

$$7\Sigma y^2 - (\Sigma y)^2 = 23\,060.28 \text{ cm}^2.$$

y plotted against x, figure 3.6, does indeed show a linear relationship. To calculate the slope we use Equation 3.9,

$$a_7 = [7\Sigma xy - \Sigma x \Sigma y]/[7\Sigma x^2 - (\Sigma x)^2]$$

$$= 10.846 \text{ cm}.$$

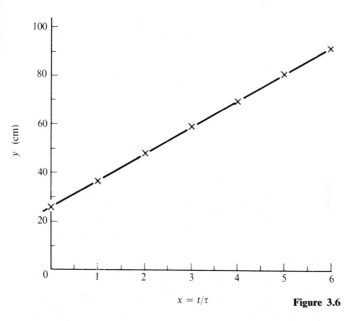

$x = t/\tau$

Figure 3.6

For the error we have, first, from Equation 3.13,

$$49\sigma_7^2(y) = 7\Sigma y^2 - (\Sigma y)^2 - [7\Sigma xy - \Sigma x\Sigma y]^2/[7\Sigma x^2 - (\Sigma x)^2]$$
$$= 3.39 \text{ cm}^2$$

and then Equation 3.11 gives the standard error of the slope,

$$S_7(a) = 7\sigma_7(y)/\{5[7\Sigma x^2 - (\Sigma x)^2]\}^{\frac{1}{2}}$$
$$= 0.059 \text{ cm}.$$

Thus the slope is

$$a = 10.846 \pm 0.059 \text{ cm}$$

and the velocity is

$$v = a/\tau = 256a = (2\,776.6 \pm 15.1) \text{ cm sec}^{-1}.$$

Since this result is derived from only 7 measurements we cannot expect the figures beyond the decimal points to be significant. Putting the standard error at 15 might still seem to be unwarranted in view of the discussion in section 2.5. However, if we think of the 15 as not precise to the last figure, but distinguishable from 10 or 20, we can express the result as

$$v = (2\,775 \pm 15)\ \text{cm sec}^{-1},$$

where the numbers are significant to 5 cm sec^{-1}.

Note that when x has only the integral values $0, 1, \ldots, (n-1)$,

$$\Sigma x = n(n-1)/2, \qquad \Sigma x^2 = n(n-1)(2n-1)/6$$

and

$$n\Sigma x^2 - (\Sigma x)^2 = n^2(n^2-1)/12. \qquad (3.31)$$

Thus the detailed calculation of this last expression can be avoided. In many experiments it is possible to measure one variable at equally spaced steps of the other, as in this example, and the calculations are thereby made somewhat simpler.

3.7.2 (See page 67)

It can be seen from the preceding example that considerable calculation is required for evaluating the best straight line. Moreover, rather more figures need to be retained in the calculations than might at first seem necessary, for, if the linear relationship *is* well obeyed,

$$n\Sigma y^2 - (\Sigma y)^2 \quad \text{and} \quad [n\Sigma xy - \Sigma x\Sigma y]^2/[n\Sigma x^2 - (\Sigma x)^2]$$

will be large but nearly equal numbers. It is their difference which gives $\sigma_n(y)$ and therefore a high precision is required for each. The use of an electronic calculator is very welcome in these circumstances.

If the labour is thought too great, some estimate can be made by drawing through the points the straight line judged 'best' by eye. It is a help here to note that, from Equation 3.3, this line should pass through the point X_n, Y_n—the centroid of the plotted points. The error may be deduced from two further straight lines, again judged by eye to be the extreme lines that could 'reasonably accord' with the points. Such procedures, of course, will yield only subjective estimates.

3.7.3 (See page 67)

Very often two physical quantities, if plotted directly, would not show a linear relationship. However, it is a great convenience if functions of the quantities can be formed which are related linearly, since the results of section 3.3 can then be employed.

Example 12

The amplitude, d, of a damped pendulum is expected to show an exponential decay with time, t:

$$d = d_0 \exp(-\gamma t).$$

Obtain a linear expression relating the variables d and t and show how this may be used to determine the decay constant, γ.

Taking logarithms of the given relation,

$$\log_e d = \log_e d_0 - \gamma t$$

or, since base 10 logarithms are more easily available for calculation,

$$\log_{10} d = \log_{10} d_0 - (\log_{10} e)\gamma t.$$

Thus if $\log_{10} d$ is plotted against t, the points should lie on a straight line of slope $\gamma \log_{10} e$.

3.7.4 (See page 67)

We have not discussed the case where x as well as y can be in error. The full least squares treatment of this, while in principle not difficult, results in extremely complicated expressions and very few experiments justify its use. When in doubt it is worth using the results of section 3.3 first assuming that only y is in error, then only x, and comparing the results to see whether there is any discrepancy. this is particularly true if the line is nearly parallel to one or other of the axes.

3.7.5 Example 13 (See page 76)

Three experiments to measure the charge of the electron gave (in coulombs) the results $(1.602 \pm 0.003) \times 10^{-19}$, $(1.607 \pm 0.004) \times 10^{-19}$, $(1.603 \pm 0.002) \times 10^{-19}$. What is their best combined estimate?

The weights of the three results are proportional to $(0.003 \times 10^{-19})^{-2} = 1.111 \times 10^{43}$, $(0.004 \times 10^{-19})^{-2} = 0.625 \times 10^{43}$, $(0.002 \times 10^{-19})^{-2} = 2.500 \times 10^{43}$. Hence the combined result giving least error is, from Equation 3.29,

$$Q = \frac{1.111 \times 1.602 + 0.625 \times 1.607 + 2.500 \times 1.603}{1.111 + 0.625 + 2.500} \times 10^{-19}$$

$$= 1.6033 \times 10^{-19} \text{ coulomb.}$$

From equation 3.30 its standard error is given by

$$S^{-2} = (1.111 + 0.625 + 2.500) \times 10^{43} \text{ coulomb}^{-2}$$

or

$$S = 0.0015 \times 10^{-19} \text{ coulomb}.$$

Thus the best combined estimate is

$$Q = (1.6035 \pm 0.0015) \times 10^{-19} \text{ coulomb}$$

(with a significance of 0.0005×10^{-19} coulomb).

3.8 PROBLEMS

17. If $z = xy$, and n measurements are made of x and m of y, show that
the least squares best estimate of the true value of z is $X_n Y_m$.

18. Successive masses of 1 kg were hung from a wire and the position of a
mark at its lower end was measured, with the following results:

Load (kg)	0	1	2	3	4	5	6	7
Position of mark (cm)	6.12	6.20	6.26	6.32	6.37	6.44	6.50	6.57

Determine the slope of the best straight line fitting these observations.

It is expected that the extension of the wire, d, is related to the
force, F, stretching it by the equation

$$F/A = Yd/l,$$

where l and A are the length and area of the unstretched wire, and Y
is the Young's modulus of the material.

If $l = 101.4 \pm 0.1$ cm and $A = (1.62 \pm 0.02) \times 10^{-5}$ cm^2 what value
does the experiment give for Y?

19. A vessel containing hydrogen was immersed in a thermostatically
controlled bath. At each of a number of temperatures the pressure of
the hydrogen was adjusted as follows to maintain a constant volume:

Temperature (°C)	10.0	15.0	20.0	25.0	30.0	35.0	40.0	45.0	50.0
Pressure (mm) of mercury)	79.2	80.7	82.0	83.5	84.6	86.3	87.7	89.2	90.4

If the absolute zero of temperature is defined as that for which the
pressure would be zero, what value does this experiment give for it?

20. Show that the measurements of Problem 12 (page 59) show an approximately linear relationship when plotted against node number and determine the wave-length and its standard error.

21. The period T and length l of a simple pendulum are theoretically related by

$$T = 2\pi(l/g)^{\frac{1}{2}}.$$

What functions of T and l would you plot to show a linear relationship that could support this theory? If the following results are obtained, what is the value of g, assuming l to be measured without error:

l (cm)	25.2	35.2	49.6	56.0	63.2	72.4
T (sec)	1.0	1.2	1.4	1.5	1.6	1.7

Do you obtain a significantly different value if the T values are assumed to be accurate and only l in error?

22. Three determinations of the velocity of light are $(2.9976 \pm 0.0005) \times 10^{10}$, $(2.9969 \pm 0.0008) \times 10^{10}$ and $(2.9984 \pm 0.0007) \times 10^{10}$ cm sec^{-1}. What is the combined estimate and its standard error?

23. Two experiments to measure the same quantity, x, involve n and m measurements and yield the values X_n, X_m, and s_n, s_m, respectively for the means and the adjusted r.m.s. deviations. Show that, according to Equation 3.29, the least squares estimate of the true value is

$$X_{n,m} = \frac{1}{n/s_n^2 + m/s_m^2}\left(\frac{nX_n}{s_n^2} + \frac{mX_m}{s_m^2}\right).$$

24. Ten measurements of the mass of the moon, using method A, give the result $(7.33 \pm 0.03) \times 10^{25}$ g and 10 measurements, using method B, give $(7.4 \pm 0.1) \times 10^{25}$ g. Does the second result affect the first in any significant way? How many measurements using method B would give it a weight roughly equal to that of the first?

25. 20 men were asked how much they earned and how many cigarettes they smoked. The results were as follows, given as income in £'s per week/cigarette consumption in number per day: 30/10, 45/20, 60/20, 60/25, 80/0, 90/55, 110/40, 150/15, 150/35, 180/0, 190/45, 210/80, 210/0, 220/65, 240/40, 270/10, 280/0, 300/70, 320/0, 340/30. Plot these values, determine the line of regression of cigarette consumption on income, and the coefficient of correlation. Show how these change when a) non-smokers, b) non-smokers and those with weekly incomes over £250, are excluded. How would you interpret these results?

26. n measurements, x_i, of a quantity x are made in one experiment and m measurements, x_j', of the same quantity are made in a second experiment of equal precision. Show that the principle of least squares applied to the sum

$$E = \sum_{i=1}^{n}(x_i - X)^2 + \sum_{j=1}^{m}(x_j' - X)^2,$$

in which all the individual errors are accorded equal weight, gives for the best combined value of x

$$X_{n,m} = \frac{nX_n + mX_m}{n + m},$$

and that this agrees with the result of Problem 23 in the special case $s_n = s_m$.

27. In Problem 26 suppose that the two experiments are of unequal precision, so that the two sets of measurements have different adjusted r.m.s. deviations, s_n and s_m. Show that we must now use the sum

$$E = \frac{1}{s_n^2} \sum_{i=1}^{n} (x_i - X)^2 + \frac{1}{s_m^2} \sum_{j=1}^{m} (x_i' - X)^2$$

for the principle of least squares to yield the result 3.29. Note that this means that we must give each individual error a weight inversely proportional to (the best estimate of) the standard deviation of the experiment from which it arises.

CHAPTER 4

Causes of error

So far we have simply accepted, as an experimental observation, the fact that any apparatus will give a variety of answers when used to make repeated measurements of what we believe to be the same physical quantity. Why should it not always give the true answer?

4.1 SYSTEMATIC ERRORS

It is clear how some errors may arise. For example, a micrometer may have a zero error, reading 0.02 mm when the jaws are closed. Suppose five measurements of the length of a metal rod, L, were 8.76, 8.76, 8.75, 8.74 and 8.74 mm. The mean of these—8.75 mm—would obviously be an incorrect 'best estimate' of L. We ought to subtract the zero error (either from each measurement or from the average) to give 8.73 mm. Moreover, it might have happened that the temperature was falling as the experiment proceeded so that the true value was not a fixed quantity, L, but one that varied with temperature. In this case we should have to decide on some standard temperature, say 20°C, at which L was to be estimated and then, either from a subsidiary experiment or from knowing the coefficient of expansion of the metal, correct the measurements accordingly.

Such errors are called systematic errors. There is no strict definition of systematic errors, since what is a systematic error for one experiment may not be for another. Very often they are constant or at least vary slowly over the time required to make a single measurement. Much of the skill in experimental work comes from eliminating sources of systematic error, or from recognizing its existence from a small sample of measurements. In the above example the adjustment should have been made to give no zero error before measurements were made and again afterwards to ensure that it had not changed. Moreover, the steady decrease in the five readings should have alerted us and, if it should continue for another five, should make us consider whether what we are measuring is truly changing with time.

4.2 RANDOM ERRORS

Nevertheless, when all systematic errors have either been eliminated or corrected for, we still do not obtain identical 'true' measurements for a repeated set of readings. The errors that the remaining variations indicate are called random errors. Just as we cannot strictly define systematic errors, so random errors, which are those that are left after the systematic ones have been accounted for, are not a well-defined class. They may arise from ambiguities or uncertainties in the process of measurement, or from fluctuations which are too irregular or fast to be observed in detail.

We will consider two examples of random error that might arise in measuring the position of a galvanometer spot on a scale graduated in milimetres. One comes from the person reading the scale and one from the galvanometer itself. Suppose the observer's eyesight is such that he can really only see that the spot is between two millimetre graduations, so that he is equally likely to say that the spot is at 11 or 12 mm when in fact it is anywhere between the two. This is not an unreasonable supposition, although for most of us this uncertainty sets in at somewhat less than 1 mm divisions.

Suppose in addition that the galvanometer has a faulty movement that either stops the spot 0.5 mm below its true value or allows it to overswing and stop 0.5 mm above. This effect is irregular or random and is unbiased, by which we mean that an error of either sign is equally likely to occur when a measurement is made.

The essential point about random errors is that with the *apparatus as it stands* no *particular* random error can be predicted or corrected for. This does not mean that the apparatus could not be improved in such a way as to eliminate some sources of random errors. And, of course, once the precision of the apparatus has been estimated this gives some idea of the average magnitude of the errors involved, but it still gives no precise information about the error of any particular single measurement.

4.3 COMBINATION OF TWO RANDOM ERRORS

To see how random errors can give the sort of results we observe, we will suppose that only the two errors described above affect the reading of the galvanometer spot when it should be at a true position of 11.000 ... mm.

Because of the random galvanometer error, the spot position will be either 10.500 ... mm or 11.500 ... mm, with equal chances for both. The observer, once more with equal probability, will read the former as 10 mm or 11 mm, and the latter as 11 mm or 12 mm. If we think of each error as a negative or positive one then the reading 10 mm will come from a negative galvanometer error combined with a negative observer error; the reading 11 mm either from a negative galvanometer error combined with a posi-tive observer error, or from a positive galvanometer error com-bined with a negative observer error; and the reading 12 mm from a combination of two positive errors. Diagrammatically we can demonstrate this as in figure 4.1.

Each final reading can be reached by one or more paths in the diagram, starting from the true value 11.000 ... mm. There are four paths altogether—the thickened line is the one corresponding to the combination of a negative galvanometer error and a positive observer error.

We can see from this that there are three possible readings: 10, 11 or 12 mm. Just which will occur in any set of measurements we cannot say, for the nature of random errors is such that we cannot tell which particular combination will occur at the time of any particular measurement. However, we have said that negative and positive errors are equally probable, and therefore all paths in this diagram are equally probable. This means that as we increase the number of readings and count the number of times each path occurs, then (occurrence of path 1):(occurrence of path

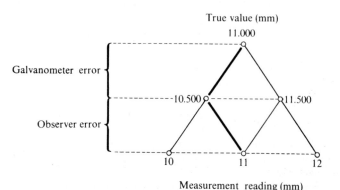

True value (mm)

11.000

Galvanometer error

10.500   11.500

Observer error

10   11   12

Measurement reading (mm)

Figure 4.1

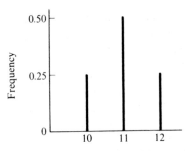

Galvanometer spot position (mm)   **Figure 4.2**

2) : (occurrence of path 3) : (occurrence of path 4) will approach the ratios $1:1:1:1$.

Now, while the 10 mm and 12 mm readings can be reached by only one path each, the 11 mm reading can be reached by two. Consequently it has twice the probability of occurring as do the other two. The (relative) frequency distribution we would expect from this model is shown in figure 4.2.

A symbolic way of looking at this is to specify a negative error as a and a positive error as b. Then aa or a^2 signifies a combination of two negative errors, ab and ba a combination of a negative and a positive error, and bb or b^2 a combination of two positive errors. So, corresponding to each possible reading we have

Measurement reading (mm)	Path No.	Symbol	Probability
10	1	aa	$\frac{1}{4}$
11	2, 3	ab, ba	$\frac{1}{2}$
12	4	bb	$\frac{1}{4}$

Now let us look at the simple quadratic expression

$$(\tfrac{1}{2})^2(a+b)^2 = \tfrac{1}{4}[aa + (ab + ba) + bb] = \tfrac{1}{4}a^2 + \tfrac{1}{2}ab + \tfrac{1}{4}b^2,$$

where a, b have the properties of ordinary numbers: $aa = a^2$, $ab = ba$, etc. We see that the products a^2, ab or ba, and b^2 correspond to the symbols of the third column and the numerical coefficients $\tfrac{1}{4}, \tfrac{1}{2}, \tfrac{1}{4}$ to the probabilities of the fourth column of the preceding table.

We can also see from this how probabilities are combined. The probability of a or b is $\frac{1}{2}$ each. The probability of a path aa, for which *a and a* are required, is the *product* of the probabilities for each stage, that is $\frac{1}{2} \times \frac{1}{2} = \frac{1}{4}$, as it is for each of the paths *ab, ba* and *bb*. The measurement 11 mm can result from either of the two different paths *ab* and *ba* each with a probability $\frac{1}{4}$. The probability for the occurrence of *ab* or *ba* is the *sum* of their separate probabilities, that is $\frac{1}{4} + \frac{1}{4} = \frac{1}{2}$.

This picture is, of course, too simple to describe most experiments and in the next chapter it will be developed and used as the basis for a more extensive 'theory' of errors. However, even this simple quadratic frequency distribution has features worth noting:

1. It is symmetrical and single peaked, which accords with the properties assumed in section 1.3.

2. The mean value 11 mm *is* the true value.

3. Each error would by itself give a two-valued distribution with standard deviation 0.5 mm. The overall standard deviation is $\sigma = 1/2^{\frac{1}{2}} = 0.707$ mm.

4.3.1 Matching errors

We may also use this model to give some guidance on how to set about reducing random errors and the allied problem of the number of significant figures to give for a measurement. Suppose that we decide to improve the precision of the apparatus by cleaning the movement, and that this brings the galvanometer error down to ±0.1 mm.

The error diagram will now be as in figure 4.3. The final row is unchanged—there is a $\frac{1}{4}, \frac{1}{2}, \frac{1}{4}$ probability of reading the values 10, 11, 12 mm and the value $\sigma = 0.707$ mm still holds. We have not,

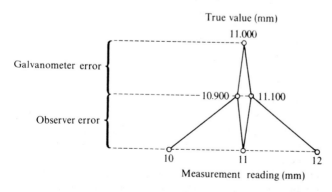

Figure 4.3

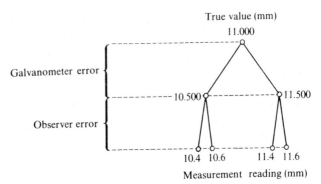

Figure 4.4

therefore, improved the precision of the apparatus (remember that the observer is counted as part of the apparatus).

Suppose, alternatively, we reduce the observer's error in the ratio $1:5$ by putting in subdivisions at 0.2 mm intervals and supplying him with a magnifying glass so that he can just see when the galvanometer spot lies between two of these. We then have the diagram in figure 4.4, which indicates a $\frac{1}{4}, \frac{1}{4}, \frac{1}{4}, \frac{1}{4}$ probability for the values 10.4, 10.6, 11.4 and 11.6 mm. The mean will be 11 mm and the standard deviation $\sigma = 0.509$ mm.

Thus neither single improvement has given the apparatus any markedly greater precision. However, if we now reduce both errors simultaneously by the same ratio $1:5$ we shall have figure 4.5 which shows that the apparatus will yield a $\frac{1}{4}, \frac{1}{2}, \frac{1}{4}$ probability for 10.8, 11.0, 11.2 mm. This has the same mean, 11.0 mm, but a standard deviation $\sigma = 0.141$ mm. So the overall precision is now also improved by a factor of five.

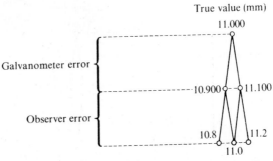

Figure 4.5

We can see from this the importance of matching the sources of random errors—there is no point in reducing any one much below the level of the others. [See §4.4.1, below]

4.3.2 Number of significant figures

We have seen in sections 2.4 and 2.5 how, when the mean and error of an experiment are calculated, the number of significant figures is limited by the precision of the apparatus and the number of measurements. There is also no point in recording measurements to more significant figures than individual errors warrant. Clearly, the observer in the first and second cases considered in section 4.3.1 would only be guessing if he were to write 10.7, 11.3, . . . mm and it would be misleading even to write 10.0, 11.0, 12.0 mm, since, as we saw in section 1.5.6, the presence of a number, even zero, after the decimal point would normally imply some possibility of differentiating between two values only 0.1 mm apart unless the contrary were stated. But even in the third case, recording for both of the possible readings 10.4 and 10.6 the same value 10.5, recording for 11.4 and 11.6 the same value 11.5, would give the same mean and make very little difference to the standard deviation. So the observer could deliberately give his results with a significance of 0.5 mm, instead of the 0.2 mm that the scale divisions and magnifying glass warrant, without materially affecting the results of the experiment. Of course, this deliberate downgrading of the apparent accuracy with which individual readings can be made is possible only if it is known beforehand that there are random errors considerably greater than this, or if an initial sample of readings shows that they have a spread of values much greater than the least significant figure of individual readings.

It would, for example, be reasonable to continue reading the values 1.53, 1.52, 1.55, 1.54, 1.53, . . . to two places of decimals, but 1.16, 1.27, 1.57, 1.36, 1.54 could be shortened to 1.2, 1.3, 1.6, 1.4, 1.5, and continued with only one place of decimals, with no important loss of information. The mean, however, as we have already seen, may well be calculated to a greater number of significant figures if enough measurements are made. [See §4.4.2, page 92]

4.4 COMMENTS AND WORKED EXAMPLE

4.4.1 Example 14 (See above)

An observer attempts to measure the velocity of a river in flood by timing the passage of floating trees over a distance of 100 m.

Using the second hand of a cheap wristwatch he records times of 26, 28, 26, 29, 27, 28, 27 sec. Would he obtain a better result if he used an expensive wristwatch with a large second hand moving over graduations marked in $\frac{1}{5}$ sec?

There are at least four possible sources of error: (i) the graduations of the time scale, (ii) variations in the watch rate, (iii) the indefinite position of a tree swirling in a flood stream, (iv) the difficulty of looking at a distant tree and the moving second hand simultaneously.

The fluctuations of 1 to 2 sec between measurements will not be changed appreciably simply by putting in $\frac{1}{5}$ sec graduations. Both (iii) and (iv) will be unaltered by changing the watch. Consequently the change will be worth while only if the fluctuations arise mainly from (ii). Now even a cheap watch is unlikely to change its rate by approximately 1 part in 30 (corresponding to 48 minutes in 1 day) in the course of a few minutes. We can therefore assume that the random errors arise from (iii) and (iv) and they will not be diminished appreciably by using a better watch.

Of course, the watch may run steadily slow or fast and this could introduce a systematic error which a better one might not suffer from. However, we should need a standard clock to check this point—even a good watch could be incorrectly adjusted.

4.4.2 (See page 91)

The main point we wish to make here is that measurements should be considered, while they are being made, in the context of the particular experiment which yields them and not simply churned out, without thought, and put straight into a formula for best estimates. To show how wrong this is, we can go right back to Robinson's five measurements, 1.52, 1.50, 1.51, 1.53 and 1.51 sec. If the scale of the instrument had been too coarse or if Robinson for some other reason had decided to give only one place of decimals, these would have been 1.5, 1.5, 1.5, 1.5 and 1.5 sec. An unthinking use of the expressions obtained earlier would give $\sigma_5 = 0$, indicating that the apparatus was quite precise, and would give for the period $T = (1.5000 \pm 0.0000)$ sec—a result of apparently perfect accuracy.

These would be obviously absurd conclusions. All we could reasonably say after the first few identical readings would be

that the recording instrument (and this might include the observer himself) was inadequate for the precision of the apparatus as a whole, and that the true errors were less than the
least significant figure recorded—0.1 sec.

4.5 PROBLEMS

28. Suppose that the galvanometer considered in sections 4.2 and 4.3 is
three times more likely to read 0.5 mm low than 0.5 mm high and that
the observer is three times more likely to say that the spot is at the
upper than at the lower of two millimetre graduations when it is
anywhere between them. Show that a true position of 11.000 . . . mm
will now be observed as 10, 11 or 12 mm with probabilities $\frac{3}{16}$, $\frac{10}{16}$ and
$\frac{3}{16}$, respectively.

29. Two experiments, A and B, to measure a certain length gave for their
first ten measurements (in cm) the following:

    A: 7.24   7.31   7.29   7.28   7.25   7.26   7.30   7.25   7.26   7.29
    B: 7.51   7.18   7.26   7.34   7.45   7.32   7.21   7.12   7.25   7.48

    From inspection do you think it is justified to record the second
    decimal place in either or both experiments? Check your opinion by
    calculating the mean and standard deviations for both sets of measure-
    ments, (i) as they stand, and (ii) with each corrected to one decimal
    place.

30. Four sets of measurements were made of Young's modulus for a
sample of aluminium alloy under different conditions and using different methods. The results were, in lb wt in$^{-2} \times 10^{-7}$:

A	1.0	1.1	1.1	1.1	1.1	1.1	1.1	1.1
B	1.04	1.11	1.10	1.09	1.12	1.09	1.10	1.11
C	1.06	0.92	1.18	1.25	1.32	1.17	1.43	0.83
D	1.43	1.32	1.25	1.18	1.17	1.06	0.92	0.83

Each set of measurements is given in the order in which it was made.
Calculate the mean and standard error in each case, and discuss their
interpretation.

31. Five judges, using hand-operated stopwatches graduated to 0.1 sec,
timed the winner of a 100 m race at 10.1, 10.0, 10.2, 10.1, 10.2 sec,
and declared the result to be 10.1 sec. A critic pointed out that since a
runner covers approximately 1 m in 0.1 sec, and since his position can
be determined by the judges much more precisely than this, the
stopwatches should be graduated to 0.01 sec and the result given to
two places of decimals. Do you agree, and if not can you suggest
alternative methods by which a more accurate result could be
achieved?

CHAPTER 5

Elementary theory of errors

In section 4.3 we saw how a frequency distribution of measurement errors could arise from a combination of only two sources of random error of a very simple mathematical nature.

In this chapter we shall extend this idea by finding the result of combining a large number of small random errors. If we take this process to the limit by decreasing the magnitude of each error while increasing indefinitely their number we shall obtain theoretical frequency distributions which are a good approximation to experimental findings.

A necessary preliminary for this is to establish the elementary statistical ideas of permutations and combinations.

5.1 PERMUTATIONS AND COMBINATIONS

Permutations concern the ordering of distinguishable objects, which we can denote by the symbols $a_1, a_2, \ldots, a_n$. They may represent anything from real objects to abstract ideas, but they must all differ from one another, and a sequence or ordering of them should have some recognizable significance. For example the eight symbols $a_1, a_2, \ldots, a_8$ could represent eight different musical notes, in which case $a_5 a_7 a_4 a_2 a_1 a_3 a_6 a_8$ would be a sequence of notes or a melody which would be recognizably different from, say, $a_5 a_7 a_2 a_4 a_1 a_3 a_6 a_8$. Or they might represent eight different instructions to a computer, in which case the two sequences would represent two distinct routines of computer operation. Or, as we shall shortly do, we may consider errors as our 'objects'.

How many different melodies are possible using each of the eight notes once only? Provided there are no rules of musical composition to hamper us, there is a choice of eight possibilities for the first note, which, once made, leaves seven for the second, which leaves six for the third, and so on down to the last note, for which there is only the one that remains after the previous seven choices have been made. Since any choice of one note can be combined with any choice of another, the number of different melodies or sequences of notes is $8 \times 7 \times 6 \times 5 \times 4 \times 3 \times 2 \times 1 = 40\,320$. Each of these is called a *permutation* of the eight notes given.

More generally, for n different objects the number of permutations is called 'factorial n' and is written

$$n! = n(n-1)(n-2)\ldots \times 2 \times 1, \qquad (5.1)$$

which is an obvious extension of the argument above.

It is not essential to label the objects solely by one suffix. The same eight notes, for example, could have been represented by a_1, a_2, a_3, b_1, b_2, b_3, b_4, b_5, where it is understood that not only do all the a's differ from each other, and the b's likewise, but that any a is different from any b. The number of permutations would still be 8! since 8 is the number of different objects.

Now suppose we decide that the a's will all be the same. Our eight-note melody will now be made up of only six different notes, five of them (the b's) occurring only once and one of them (the a's) three times. Or our eight instruction computer routine will now contain three identical instructions. Then the two melodies $a_3 b_4 a_2 b_5 b_3 b_1 a_1 b_2$ and $a_2 b_4 a_3 b_5 b_3 b_1 a_1 b_2$ will be the same, as will any other of the $3! = 6$ melodies obtained by permuting the a's among themselves while the positions of the b's remain fixed. This is true for every arrangement of the b's and reduces the number of different melodies to $8!/3! = 40\,320/6 = 6\,720$. We may drop the suffixes for the a's since they are indistinguishable, so that this number is now the number of different sequences of the type $ab_1 aab_5 b_4 b_2 b_3$, $ab_2 ab_3 b_4 ab_5 b_1$, etc.

Let us go further and now make all the b's the same, so that the eight note melody is formed of only two different notes or the routine of only two different instructions. Permutations of the five b's among themselves for any arrangement of the a's will not change the overall arrangement, so we must divide the total again, this time by $5! = 120$, and thus arrive at $8!/(3! \times 5!) = 56$ as the number of different melodies, or routines, or different sequences of the type $abbabbba$, $ababbabb$, etc.

Another way of looking at this is to say that there are eight possible positions from which we choose three at a time to be filled by the a's, the b's automatically filling the rest. The number of such *combinations* of 8 taken 3 at a time is denoted by ${}_8 C_3$, or $\binom{8}{3}$

and, as we have seen, has the value

$$_8C_3 = \binom{8}{3} = \frac{8!}{3!5!}.$$

If we had chosen the positions for the b's first—that is, the number of combinations of 8 taken 5 at a time—we should have obtained the same number of course, as is confirmed by its numerical value

$$_8C_5 = \binom{8}{5} = \frac{8!}{5!3!} = \binom{8}{3} = {}_8C_3.$$

The generalization of the discussion is clear and shows that the number of combinations of n taken r at a time is

$$_nC_r = \frac{n!}{r!(n-r)!} = {}_nC_{n-r}. \qquad (5.2)$$

5.2   BINOMIAL DISTRIBUTION

Suppose there are n sources of error, each of which can contribute very small errors $+e$ or $-e$ to the true value X. We can construct an error diagram for this as shown in figure 5.1.

The final measurements, shown on the bottom line, can clearly range from $X - ne$ to $X + ne$ in steps of $2e$. Any particular combination of errors, or path in the diagram from X to one of the

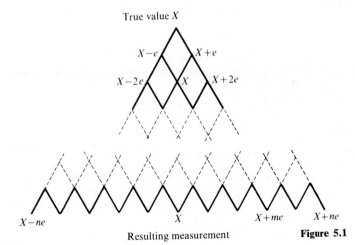

Resulting measurement

Figure 5.1

possible measurements, can be represented by a product such as $aab\ldots ba$ where a means an error to the left $(-e)$, b an error to the right $(+e)$. The product $aab\ldots ba$ would mean an error $-e$, followed by $-e$, followed by $+e$, followed by $\ldots,\ldots$, followed by $+e$, followed by $-e$. There are n factors altogether, so if r of them are b's, $n-r$ will be a's and the product can be written $a^{n-r}b^r$. This will give a measurement error $(n-r)(-e)+re = (2r-n)e$.

For any error $(2r-n)e$, or corresponding product $a^{n-r}b^r$, there are many different ways of writing out the order of the individual factors—$aab\ldots ba$, $aba\ldots ba$, etc. Each of these corresponds to a particular path in the diagram and is an equally likely way in which the error $(2r-n)e$ could arise. The number of different combinations of $n-r$ factors a and r factors b is given by Equation 5.2,

$$_nC_{n-r} = {}_nC_r = \frac{n!}{r!(n-r)!},$$

and this is just the coefficient of $a^{n-r}b^r$ in the binomial expansion

$$(a+b)^n = a^n + na^{n-1}b + \ldots + {}_nC_r a^{n-r}b^r + \ldots + nab^{n-1} + b^n.$$

Now the probability of obtaining any particular measurement error is proportional to the number of ways in which it can arise, or the number of suitable paths leading from the apex to the corresponding point on the bottom line of the diagram, if these are all equally likely, and is therefore proportional to the corresponding coefficient in the binomial expansion. To obtain the absolute probability we must divide by the sum of all these coefficients. This is simply calculated by putting $a = b = 1$ in the binomial expansion,

$$2^n = (1+1)^n = 1 + n + \ldots + {}_nC_r + \ldots + n + 1$$
$$= {}_nC_0 + {}_nC_1 + \ldots + {}_nC_r + \ldots + \ldots + {}_nC_{n-1} + {}_nC_n.$$

Hence the absolute probability of obtaining a measurement error $(2r-n)e$ is

$$2^{-n}{}_nC_r = \frac{n!}{2^n r!(n-r)!}.$$

Putting

$$(2r-n) = m \quad \text{or} \quad r = \tfrac{1}{2}(n+m),$$

we have for the probability of obtaining an error

$$\varepsilon = me,$$

or a measurement

$$x = X + \varepsilon,$$

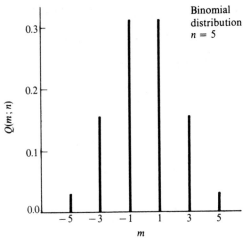

Binomial
distribution
$n = 5$

Figure 5.2

the expression

[See §5.5.1,
page 112]

$$Q(m;n) = \frac{n!}{2^n\left(\dfrac{n+m}{2}\right)!\left(\dfrac{n-m}{2}\right)!} .$$ (5.3)

Examples of this *binomial probability distribution* for various values
of n are given in figures 5.2, 5.3 and 5.4. The scale has been varied

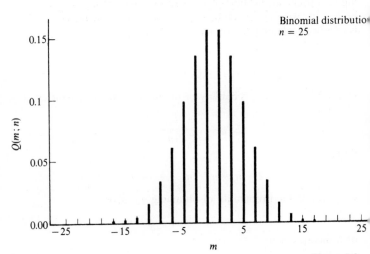

Binomial distributio⚫
$n = 25$

Figure 5.3

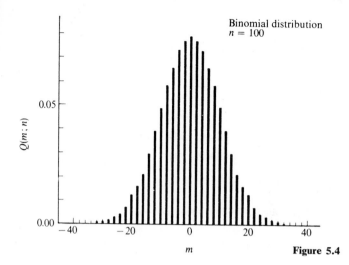

Figure 5.4

so that e decreases as n increases to give each of the distributions a comparable 'width'.

We can see that as n increases we approach a smooth, symmetrical, single-peaked distribution of just the kind discussed in section 1.3. It may be remarked that m can take only even or odd values according to whether n is even or odd, and that ε can therefore vary only in steps of $2e$. However, in what follows we shall allow e to decrease towards zero while n increases towards infinity, in which case these restrictions become unimportant.

5.3 GAUSSIAN DISTRIBUTION

Let us first examine the form of $Q(m; n)$ as n and m are increased indefinitely. n is always positive, but m can be positive or negative, so that one of the quantities $\frac{1}{2}(n+m)$ and $\frac{1}{2}(n-m)$ will be the difference between two large numbers. It could, therefore, remain quite small unless we stipulate that n must increase at a greater rate than m. If we do this—and we shall see shortly how this can be specified more precisely—all the factorials in Equation 5.3 will be very large and we can use Stirling's approximate formula for the factorial of a large number,

$$\log(\nu!) \simeq \tfrac{1}{2}\log 2\pi\nu + \nu(\log \nu - 1).$$

Then, from Equation 5.3,

$$\log Q(m;n) = \log(n!) - \log\left[\left(\frac{n+m}{2}\right)!\right]$$

$$- \log\left[\left(\frac{n-m}{2}\right)!\right] - n\log 2$$

$$\simeq \tfrac{1}{2}\log 2\pi n + n(\log n - 1)$$

$$- \tfrac{1}{2}\log[\pi(n+m)] - \tfrac{1}{2}(n+m)[\log\tfrac{1}{2}(n+m) - 1]$$

$$- \tfrac{1}{2}\log[\pi(n-m)] - \tfrac{1}{2}(n-m)[\log\tfrac{1}{2}(n-m) - 1]$$

$$- n\log 2.$$

Now

$$\log 2\pi n - \log[\pi(n+m)] - \log[\pi(n-m)]$$

$$= \log 2\pi n - \log \pi n - \log\left(1 + \frac{m}{n}\right) - \log \pi n - \log\left(1 - \frac{m}{n}\right)$$

$$= \log\frac{2}{\pi n} - \log\left(1 - \frac{m^2}{n^2}\right)$$

and

$$n(\log n - 1) - \tfrac{1}{2}(n+m)[\log\tfrac{1}{2}(n+m) - 1]$$

$$- \tfrac{1}{2}(n-m)[\log\tfrac{1}{2}(n-m) - 1] - n\log 2$$

$$= n\log n - n - \tfrac{1}{2}(n+m)\left[\log n + \log\left(1 + \frac{m}{n}\right) - \log 2 - 1\right]$$

$$- \tfrac{1}{2}(n-m)\left[\log n + \log\left(1 - \frac{m}{n}\right) - \log 2 - 1\right] - n\log 2$$

$$= -\tfrac{1}{2}n\log\left(1 - \frac{m^2}{n^2}\right) - \tfrac{1}{2}m\log\frac{1 + m/n}{1 - m/n}.$$

Hence

$$\log Q(m;n) \simeq \tfrac{1}{2}\log\frac{2}{\pi n} - \tfrac{1}{2}(n+1)\log\left(1 - \frac{m^2}{n^2}\right)$$

$$- \tfrac{1}{2}m\log\frac{1 + m/n}{1 - m/n}.$$

Now if n increases much more rapidly than m, m/n will be very small compared with unity. Hence, for large n,

$$(n+1)\log\left(1 - \frac{m^2}{n^2}\right) = (n+1)\left(-\frac{m^2}{n^2} + \ldots\right) \simeq -\frac{m^2}{n}$$

and

$$m \log \frac{1 + m/n}{1 - m/n} = m\left[\frac{m}{n} + \ldots - \left(-\frac{m}{n} + \ldots\right)\right] \simeq \frac{2m^2}{n}.$$

Then

$$\log Q(m;n) \simeq \tfrac{1}{2}\log\frac{2}{\pi n} - \frac{m^2}{2n}$$

or

$$Q(m;n) \simeq \left(\frac{2}{\pi n}\right)^{\frac{1}{2}} \exp\left(-\frac{m^2}{2n}\right). \tag{5.4}$$

Suppose we define an error distribution function $P(x)$ to represent the Gaussian distribution as n and m are increased towards infinity. Then the probability of finding a measurement in the interval $(x, x + dx)$ will be

$$P(x)\, dx = \Sigma Q(m;n),$$

where the summation is over all those possible measurements that lie in the interval $(x, x + dx)$. Since the measurement steps are $2e$ there will be $dx/2e$ of these, each with the probability given by Equation 5.4. Hence

$$P(x)\, dx \simeq \left(\frac{2}{\pi n}\right)^{\frac{1}{2}} \exp\left(-\frac{m^2}{2n}\right)\frac{dx}{2e}$$

$$\simeq \left(\frac{1}{2\pi n e^2}\right)^{\frac{1}{2}} \exp\left(-\frac{m^2 e^2}{2n e^2}\right)^{\frac{1}{2}} dx. \tag{5.5}$$

Since $m = 0$ defines the true value X, me is the error

$$x - X = \varepsilon = me.$$

We can now see how the limits should be taken so as to ensure a finite, non-zero, distribution function. e must decrease towards zero and n and m increase towards infinity while keeping ne^2 and me finite and non-zero. This also ensures that in these limiting processes n is much larger than m as the approximations above required. Thus if we define

$$\sigma^2 = ne^2, \tag{5.6}$$

Equations 5.4, 5.5 and 5.6 then give

$$P(x; X, \sigma)\, dx = \frac{1}{(2\pi)^{\frac{1}{2}}\sigma} \exp\left[-\frac{(x - X)^2}{2\sigma^2}\right] dx, \tag{5.7}$$

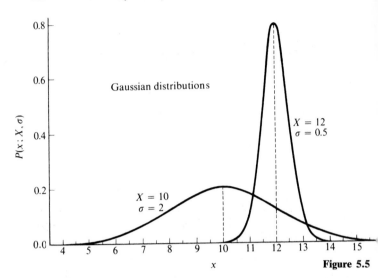

Figure 5.5

where $P(x)$ is more fully described by including the parameters, X and σ, that define the distribution.

   This distribution, which is known as the *Gaussian* or *normal* distribution, is entirely determined by the two quantities X and σ. Two examples are given in figure 5.5. The curve is symmetrical about, and peaked at, the value $x = X$ and the width of the peak diminishes with σ. All such distributions can be reduced, by changing to the variable

$$y = (x - X)/\sigma, \qquad dy = dx/\sigma, \qquad (5.8)$$

to the standard form,

[See §5.5.2, page 112]
$$\phi(y)\,dy = \frac{1}{(2\pi)^{\frac{1}{2}}} \exp\left(-\frac{y^2}{2}\right) dy. \qquad (5.9)$$

This is shown in figure 5.6 and tabulated in Appendix 1.

   The way in which the distribution has been derived ensures that it is normalized, that is

$$\int_{-\infty}^{\infty} P(x; X, \sigma)\,dx = \int_{-\infty}^{\infty} P(\varepsilon; \sigma)\,d\varepsilon = \int_{-\infty}^{\infty} \phi(y)\,dy = 1$$

$$(5.10)$$

and this can be checked by direct calculation.

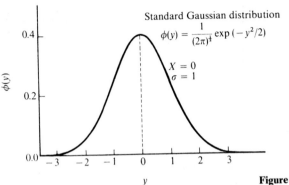

$$\phi(y) = \frac{1}{(2\pi)^{\frac{1}{2}}} \exp(-y^2/2)$$

Standard Gaussian distribution

$X = 0$
$\sigma = 1$

y

Figure 5.6

Its main properties are as follows:

1. *Mean, mode and median*. These occur at $x = X$, as is clear from the single-peaked symmetrical shape of the distribution.

2. *Standard deviation*. The standard deviation of an (infinite) set of errors distributed according to the Gaussian law is given by

$$\int_{-\infty}^{\infty} (x - X)^2 P(x; X, \sigma)\, dx = \int_{-\infty}^{\infty} \varepsilon^2 P(\varepsilon; \sigma)\, d\varepsilon = \sigma^2 \quad (5.11)$$

and this is, of course, the reason why we have used the symbol σ in our derivation. The distribution function drops by a factor $e^{-\frac{1}{2}} = 0.607$ as x recedes from X to $X \pm \sigma$.

The probability that a measurement will lie somewhere between these limits is

$$\int_{-\sigma}^{\sigma} P(\varepsilon, \sigma)\, d\varepsilon = 0.683, \quad (5.12)$$

so that the probability that it will be outside them is 0.317.

The probability that a measurement will lie within $X \pm 3\sigma$ is

$$\int_{-3\sigma}^{3\sigma} P(\varepsilon, \sigma)\, d\varepsilon = 0.997 \quad (5.13)$$

and the probability that it will lie outside them is 0.003.

We can see from this that any single measurement is quite likely to be in error by about σ but very unlikely to be in error by several times this. Both the above results are special cases of the

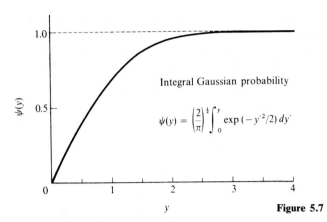

Figure 5.7

integral

$$\int_{X-\varepsilon}^{X+\varepsilon} P(x; X, \sigma)\, dx = 2\int_0^\varepsilon P(\varepsilon; \sigma)\, d\varepsilon = 2\int_0^{\varepsilon/\sigma} \phi(y')\, dy',$$

which is the probability of obtaining an error less than ε. Writing, as in Equation 5.8,

$$y = (x - X)/\sigma = \varepsilon/\sigma,$$

this probability may be expressed as

$$\int_{x-\varepsilon}^{x+\varepsilon} P(x; X; \sigma)\, dx = \psi(y),$$

where

$$\psi(y) = 2\int_0^y \phi(y')\, dy' = \left(\frac{2}{\pi}\right)^{\frac{1}{2}}\int_0^y \exp\left(-\frac{y'^2}{2}\right) dy'. \qquad (5.14)$$

This integral form of the Gaussian probability is shown in figure 5.7 and tabulated in Appendix 2.

5.4 POISSON DISTRIBUTION

It must be emphasized that when a measurement is made its error in no sense indicates a mistake. The whole physical system—the object being measured plus the apparatus used for this, and the observer—is subject to a large number of sources of small random errors. According to the binomial model we can think of all these as fluctuating between negative and positive values of equal amount and with equal probability and entirely independently of each other. Consequently, when a measurement is made this does describe the system as it actually is at that moment. When a set of such measurements is made they constitute a kind of record of the whole physical system. Often we are not directly interested in the exact form of this record, which largely depends upon the apparatus, but in the single number we can derive from it that describes the physical quantity we wish to measure. For such quantities we usually try to design apparatus, within the resources available, to give errors as small as possible, and thus produce a high precision experiment—that is, one with a small value of σ.

There are, however, many cases where the precision of the apparatus has little or no effect upon the measurements, and yet the measurements still show fluctuations of a random nature. A typical example concerns the number of dust particles or small meteorites that collide with a satellite travelling in space. Although we can speak of the average density of the particles they will not all be spaced in a regular way at equal distances from each other. Sometimes two or more will be closer than average, sometimes further apart. Consequently, during each kilometre, say, of the satellite's path the number of particles it collides with will vary. Improving the apparatus used in the satellite to count these collisions will not diminish the fluctuations between one kilometre of path and another, but simply make each count a more reliable one.

Here we are measuring a physical quantity which has an intrinsic 'error distribution', and where this distribution, rather than a single number, is its proper description. The grasshoppers' legs of section 1.3 provided another example. To obtain a model, or theory, for such cases we again use the binomial type of diagram, but with a rather different interpretation (figure 5.8).

We will start with a crude model in which we consider the condition of the satellite at each 10 m, say, of its journey and represent this by a point on the diagram. If no collision is made during the first 10 m the point moves to the left, from P to Q, but if one has occurred it moves to the right, from P to R. Q or R then represents the satellite's condition at the beginning of the second 10 m stage, and a second move to the left or the right once more indicates no collision or one collision during that stage.

After 100 such stages the kilometre journey is complete and we reach the final line of the diagram with the representative point at a distance to the right indicating the number of collisions that have occurred. Any final position can be reached, in general, by a

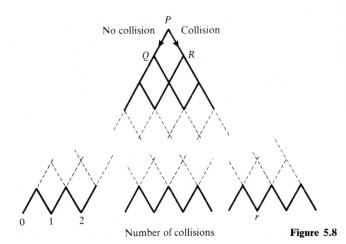

No collision   Collision

Number of collisions   **Figure 5.8**

variety of paths, each representing the history of the satellite during its successive 10 m journeys. Thus a possible path, represented as before by a product such as $baa \ldots ba$, means one collision, no collision, no collision, $\ldots$, one collision, no collision. There will be 100 factors altogether, and the number of b's will be equal to the number of collisions. More generally, a journey divided into n stages, of which r involve a collision, will be described by a product of n factors of which $n - r$ will be a's and r will be b's. The number of ways in which a total of r collisions can arise is then $_nC_{n-r}$ or $_nC_r$—the coefficient of $a^{n-r}b^r$ in the binomial expansion of $(a + b)^n$.

There is one important difference from our previous use of the binomial distribution to derive the Gaussian distribution. There the alternative directions at each point of the error diagram were equally likely, since they represented positive or negative errors that could occur with equal probability. As a result, all paths through the diagram were equally likely. This is not the case now. If the particles are stationary and their density is so low that they are spaced several tens of metres apart, and the satellite is a sphere of diameter about 1 m, the probability of a collision occurring during one stage of 10 m is clearly much less than there being no collision. If p is the probability of collision, $1 - p$ will be the probability of no collision and we shall have

$$p \ll 1 - p, \quad \text{or} \quad p \ll 1.$$

At any point of the diagram motion to the left will then have a probability $1 - p$ and motion to the right a probability p. What is the probability for a complete path through the diagram?

Starting with a right motion, or b, its probability is p. ba—that is, right motion followed by left motion—will have the probability, p, of b occurring diminished still further by the factor $(1-p)$ that represents the probability of an a following. Thus the probability of ba will be $p(1-p)$. Continuing in this way, the probability of $baa \ldots ba$ will be

$$p(1-p)(1-p) \ldots p(1-p) = p^r(1-p)^{n-r},$$

since there are r b's and $(n-r)$ a's. Thus each of the $_nC_r$ paths that leads to the total of r collisions has the *same* probability $p^r(1-p)^{n-r}$. The overall probability of r collisions occurring will be the sum of these probabilities, which we shall call

$$P(r; n, p) = p^r(1-p)^{n-r}{}_nC_r$$
$$= \frac{p^r(1-p)^{n-r}n!}{r!(n-r)!}.$$

There is a flaw in the above argument which we must now repair. When we spoke about no collision or one collision occurring during each stage we were careful to avoid any mention of *two* or even more collisions occurring. Now it is true that, if the probability for one collision is small, that for the two collisions is smaller still. But the two particles *could* be a few metres apart, in line with the satellite's trajectory, and therefore both collide with it during one 10 m stage. The only way to reduce the probability of a double collision so much as to justify our neglecting it is to make the stages infinitesimally small, which is equivalent to increasing n indefinitely. As each stage decreases so will the probability of one collision occurring in it, and we may expect that once the length is small enough the probability, p, will be proportional to it. But the length is inversely proportional to n, so there will be a reciprocal relationship between n and p which we shall write as

$$\mu = np,$$

where μ is a constant. We use Stirling's formula again to give an approximate expression for $P(r; n, p)$. Here, however, r remains a finite number while n, and therefore $n-r$, increase indefinitely:

$\log P(r; n, p)$

$$= r \log \frac{p}{1-p} + n \log(1-p) + \log n! - \log(n-r)! - \log r!$$

$$\approx r \log \frac{p}{1-p} + n \log(1-p) + \tfrac{1}{2} \log 2\pi n + n(\log n - 1)$$

$$- \tfrac{1}{2} \log 2\pi(n-r) - (n-r)[\log(n-r) - 1] - \log r!.$$

Since

$$p = \frac{\mu}{n},$$

where μ is also finite,

$$r \log \frac{p}{1-p} + n(\log n - 1) - (n-r)[\log(n-r) - 1]$$

$$= r \log \frac{\mu}{n(1-\mu/n)} + n(\log n - 1) - (n-r)$$

$$\times \left[\log n + \log \left(1 - \frac{r}{n} \right) - 1 \right]$$

$$= r \log \mu - r \log \left(1 - \frac{\mu}{n} \right) - n \log \left(1 - \frac{r}{n} \right) - r + r \log \left(1 - \frac{r}{n} \right)$$

$$= r \log \mu - r \left(-\frac{\mu}{n} + \ldots \right) - n \left(-\frac{r}{n} + \ldots \right) - r + r \left(-\frac{r}{n} + \ldots \right)$$

$$\rightarrow r \log \mu \text{ as } n \rightarrow \infty,$$

and

$$n \log(1-p) + \tfrac{1}{2} \log 2\pi n - \tfrac{1}{2} \log 2\pi(n-r)$$

$$= n \log \left(1 - \frac{\mu}{n} \right) - \tfrac{1}{2} \log \left(1 - \frac{r}{n} \right)$$

$$= n \left(-\frac{\mu}{n} + \ldots \right) - \tfrac{1}{2} \left(-\frac{r}{n} + \ldots \right)$$

$$\rightarrow -\mu \text{ as } n \rightarrow \infty.$$

Hence, as n increases towards infinity,

$$\log P(r; n, p) \rightarrow \log P(r; \mu) = -\mu + r \log \mu - \log r!$$

or

$$P(r; \mu) = e^{-\mu} \mu^r / r!, \qquad (5.15)$$

which is known as the *Poisson distribution*.

The Poisson distribution differs in three important respects from the Gaussian. Firstly, it refers to a discrete variable, r, that can take only zero or positive integral values, unlike the continuous measurement variable x. As we may expect from our satellite experiment, it is commonly concerned with counting processes such as the number of cosmic ray particles detected during equal

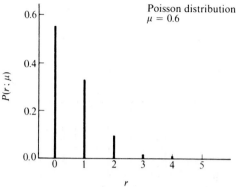

Figure 5.9

intervals of time. Secondly, it is not symmetrical. Examples are given in figures 5.9, 5.10, 5.11 and 5.12 and in Appendix 3. They show that when μ is small the asymmetry is very marked, but that as μ increases the distributions steadily become more symmetrical. Thirdly, the distribution is completely determined by the one parameter, μ.

$P(r;\mu)$ is normalized by virtue of its derivation or it may be shown directly as follows:

$$\sum_{r=0}^{\infty} P(r;\mu) = \sum_{r=0}^{\infty} e^{-\mu}\mu^r/r!$$

$$= e^{-\mu}\sum_{r=0}^{\infty} \mu^r/r!$$

$$= e^{-\mu}e^{\mu} = 1. \qquad (5.16)$$

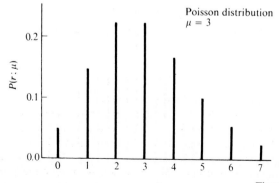

Figure 5.10

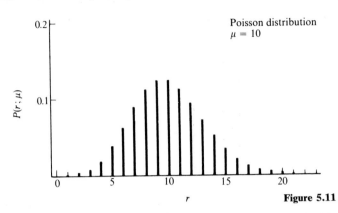

Figure 5.11

The various properties of the distribution can all be described in terms of μ. In particular we may calculate the following:

1. *The most probable value*, mode:

$$\frac{P(r;\mu)}{P(r-1;\mu)} = \frac{e^{-\mu}\mu^r}{r!} \cdot \frac{(r-1)!}{e^{-\mu}\mu^{r-1}} = \frac{\mu}{r}.$$

Hence, as long as r is less than μ, $P(r;\mu)$ increases with r but, once r exceeds μ, $P(r;\mu)$ will decrease with r. Thus, if μ is not an integer, $P(r;\mu)$ has its maximum value at

$$r = \{\mu\}, \tag{5.17}$$

where $\{\mu\}$ is the greatest integer less than μ. If μ is an integer, $P(r;\mu)$ will have two equal maxima at

$$r = \mu - 1 \quad \text{and} \quad r = \mu. \tag{5.18}$$

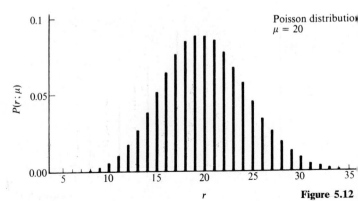

Figure 5.12

2. *The mean value*:

$$\bar{r} = \sum_{r=0}^{\infty} rP(r;\mu)$$

$$= e^{-\mu} \sum_{r=0}^{\infty} \frac{r\mu^r}{r!}$$

$$= \mu e^{-\mu} \sum_{s=0}^{\infty} \frac{\mu^s}{s!} \qquad (s = r-1)$$

$$= \mu e^{-\mu} e^{\mu} = \mu. \qquad\qquad (5.19)$$

[See §5.5.3, page 113]

3. *The standard deviation*:

$$\overline{r^2} = \sum_{r=0}^{\infty} r^2 P(r;\mu)$$

$$= e^{-\mu} \sum_{r=0}^{\infty} \frac{r^2 \mu^r}{r!}$$

$$= \mu e^{-\mu} \left[\sum_{s=0}^{\infty} \frac{s\mu^s}{s!} + \sum_{s=0}^{\infty} \frac{\mu^s}{s!} \right]$$

$$= \mu^2 e^{-\mu} e^{\mu} + \mu e^{-\mu} e^{\mu}$$

$$= \mu^2 + \mu.$$

Hence, from Equation 1.12,

$$\sigma^2 = \overline{r^2} - (\bar{r})^2 = \mu,$$

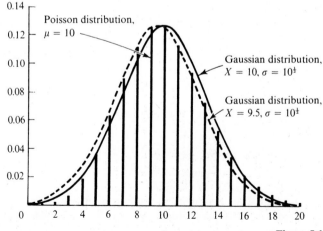

Figure 5.13

[See §5.5.4,
page 115] or

$$\sigma = \mu^{\frac{1}{2}}. \qquad (5.20)$$

The Poisson distribution becomes not simply more symmetrical as μ increases—it approaches a Gaussian form with mean μ and standard deviation $\mu^{\frac{1}{2}}$. Figure 5.13 shows that even for $\mu = 10$ the Gaussian shape is a reasonable approximation. Because of the slight remaining asymmetry a rather better fit around the peak is obtained if the Gaussian distribution is displaced a little towards lower values. For $\mu \gtrsim 30$ the asymmetry is negligible and the fit is very close.

5.5 COMMENTS AND WORKED EXAMPLES

5.5.1 Example 15 (See page 98)

What is the most probable error for the binomial distribution?

Since m can vary only in steps of 2, the ratio of neighbouring probabilities is

$$\frac{Q(m+2;n)}{Q(m;n)} = \frac{[(n+m)/2]![(n-m)/2]!}{[(n+m+2)/2]![(n-m-2)/2]!} = \frac{n-m}{n+m+2}.$$

Then

$$Q(m+2;n) \gtreqless Q(m;n)$$

according as

$$n-m \gtreqless n+m+2 \quad \text{or} \quad m \lesseqgtr -1.$$

If n is even, m is even. Therefore Q is increasing beyond $m = \ldots -4, -2$, and decreasing beyond $m = 0, 2, 4, \ldots$. So the most probable error occurs at $m = 0$ and is zero.

If n is odd, m is odd. Therefore Q is increasing beyond $m = \ldots -7, -5, -3$, and decreasing beyond $m = 1, 3, 5, \ldots$. The greatest probabilities therefore occur at $m = \pm 1$ and are equal for the errors $\pm e$.

5.5.2 Example 16 (See page 102)

Compare the measurements of Example 2 (page 21) with the appropriate Gaussian distribution.

The best estimates of mean and standard deviation were calculated in Example 4 (page 48) as $X_{16} = 33.488$ m and $s_{16} = 0.0166$ m and these will be the X and σ of the required

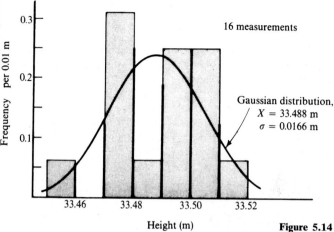

Height (m)

Figure 5.14

curve. Equations 5.8 show that we can construct the relevant Gaussian curve from the standard form (Appendix 1) by transferring its centre to the value 33.488, scaling the x-axis by the factor 0.0166 and the y-axis by $1/0.0166 = 60$. However, to accord with histogram intervals of 0.01 m, the y-axis must be further scaled by 0.01 to give an overall factor 0.6.

This gives us figure 5.14, in which the results are also plotted as the distribution of figure 1.19 and the histogram of figure 1.20.

5.5.3 (See page 111)

Our illustration of the Poisson distribution can be thought of most simply in terms of fixed dust particles and a moving satellite. Suppose the area of the satellite at right angles to its direction of motion is A, and suppose we are counting the number of collisions, r, in successive paths of length l. r will then be the number of particles in the cylinder of cross-section area A and length l swept out by the satellite. The average of a very large number of such counts is, from Equation 5.19, μ, which is equivalent to saying that the average density of the dust particles is $\mu/(Al)$.

Thus if this average density is ν particles per unit volume the *average* number of particles in a volume V will be νV, but the numbers, q, that will actually be in particular volumes V will vary from one volume to another according to the Poisson distribution

$$P(q; \nu, V) = e^{-\nu V}(\nu V)^q/q!.$$

Suppose now instead of a moving satellite we had a stationary detector with particles streaming towards it. There would be an average rate of particles, η per unit time, impinging on the detector and therefore ηT would be the *average* number detected in intervals of time T. The actual numbers counted, q, would again follow the Poisson distribution

$$P(q; \eta, T) = e^{-\eta T}(\eta T)^q/q!.$$

The essential idea behind the Poisson distribution is that the processes that are counted or observed are random—that is, independent of each other. Thus the fact that the satellite makes or does not make a collision at a certain point of its path makes no difference to its chances of making any subsequent collisions. It is important to realize that a mean number of counts, η per unit time, *does not* imply that the probability of recording a count in any time interval τ is $\eta\tau$. Over many time intervals τ the *mean* will be $\eta\tau$, but the probability of finding just *one* count in any such interval, when the mean is $\eta\tau$, will be, using the Poisson distribution (5.12),

$$P(1; \eta\tau) = \eta\tau e^{-\eta\tau}.$$

Only when τ is so small that

$$\eta\tau \ll 1$$

can we use the approximation

$$P(1; \eta\tau) = \eta\tau(1 - \eta\tau + \ldots) \simeq \eta\tau,$$

and thus assert that the probability is proportional to the time interval.

Example 17

What is the distribution function for t, the time interval between successive counts, when the mean number of counts per unit time is η? The problem is that of finding no counts in an interval t, followed by a single count in the next interval dt. Since the mean numbers in the two cases are ηt and $\eta\, dt$, and the two events (no count followed by one count) are independent, the overall probability is the product of the two relevant

Poisson distributions,

$$P(0; \eta t)P(1; \eta \, dt) = e^{-\eta t}\eta \, dt e^{-\eta dt}$$
$$\simeq \eta e^{-\eta t} \, dt \quad \text{for small } dt.$$

Since the distribution function $f(t)$ is so defined that $f(t) \, dt$ is the probability of obtaining a value between t and $t + dt$,

$$f(t) \, dt = \eta e^{-\eta t} \, dt.$$

Thus the required function is $\eta e^{-\eta t}$. (Since t refers to the time interval between one count and the *next* the function derived above must necessarily refer only to positive values of t—to be formal we should add $f(t) = 0$ for $t < 0$.)

5.5.4 (See page 112)

Equation 5.20 is an important result. It shows that counts of random processes may be expected to show fluctuations of the order of their square roots. This helps in judging whether a particular count is consistent with a predicted number. Thus a count of 8 cosmic ray particles in one hour is quite consistent with the statement that the average rate is $10 \, \text{hr}^{-1}$, since the difference is only $10 - 8 = 2$ compared with an expected fluctuation of $10^{\frac{1}{2}} = 3.16$. However, if 800 were measured in 100 hours, it would be most unlikely that the average rate was $10 \, \text{hr}^{-1}$. If it were we should expect 1000 in 100 hours, with fluctuations of the order of $1000^{\frac{1}{2}} = 31.6$. The difference $1000 - 800 = 200$ is over six times as large.

5.6 PROBLEMS

32. The volume of a steel block was found by repeatedly immersing it in water and measuring the amount displaced. Successive measurements were 110.7, 111.0, 110.9, 110.5, 111.1, 110.8, 111.1, 110.9, 111.2, 110.6, 110.5, 110.0, 110.8, 11.09, 110.5, 111.2, 110.4, 110.8, 111.1, 110.7 cm³. Do you think that these results are evidence of a Gaussian distribution of errors?

33. A similar experiment to find the volume of a wooden block (held under to make sure it was completely immersed each time) gave measurements 110.2, 110.4, 110.3, 110.6, 110.5, 110.8, 110.6, 110.9, 111.2, 110.9, 111.0, 111.1, 111.3, 111.0, 111.3, 111.5, 111.2, 111.4, 111.2, 111.3 cm³. How would you interpret these results?

34. Liquid containing cells of type A was spread on a slide and examined systematically under a microscope. One hundred counts of cells in

1 mm × 1 mm squares were made with the following frequencies:

Count	0	1	2	3	4	5	6	7	8	9	10	11	12...
Frequency	1	3	8	14	17	19	14	12	6	2	2	2	0...; total 100.

When cells of type B were examined the corresponding counts were:

Count	0	1	2	3	4	5	6	7	8	9...
Frequency	0	0	0	5	29	33	27	6	0	0...; total 100.

Compare these with the relevant Poisson distributions and comment on possible differences between cells A and B.

35. One hundred and forty-six children are born in a town during one year. Assuming that pregnancy is independent of seasonal effects such as the weather or the number of hours of daylight, on how many days of the year can the maternity services expect to have to deal with 3 births?

36. Two villages are linked by 12 telephone lines. The numbers of subscribers wishing to make a cell at any one time are on average 10 and it is assumed that they have a Poisson frequency distribution. On what proportion of occasions will a subscriber find it impossible to make a call because all lines are in use? How many lines will be necessary to reduce this to less than 1%? How many for less than 0.1%?

37. An electronic counter of nuclear particles has a 'dead time', τ sec, immediately following a count, during which it is insensitive to any succeeding particle. If a stream of particles arrives at random time intervals at an average rate of η particles sec^{-1}, how will the counting rate depend upon the relative values of τ and $1/\eta$?

38. Show that of n sample observations from a Gaussian distribution of standard deviation σ, we should expect n' to be in error by ε or more, where

$$\psi(\varepsilon/\sigma) = 1 - n'/n.$$

If $n' = 0.5$ is taken to mean that even one observation with this amount of error is unlikely, show that for 10 observations we are unlikely to observe any error greater than 1.96σ, and for 100 observations any greater than 2.81σ. (This is Chauvenet's criterion, sometimes used for rejecting observations whose errors are 'too great'.) What are the error limits if we take instead $n' = 0.1$?

39. Show that in an integral counting experiment where the average in a certain interval is 0.5 the probability of obtaining one or more counts is 0.393, and that if the average is 0.1 the probability is 0.095. What is the bearing of these results on Problem 38?

CHAPTER 6

Likelihood, confidence and truth

In the first three chapters we derived simple procedures for quantitatively describing the results of experiments. They were somewhat arbitrary and empirical, but nevertheless they had the virtues of consistency and of agreeing with intuitive qualitative ideas of accuracy or reliability or precision. It was what we might call a 'common sense' approach to the subject. Now that we have discussed some probability distributions we are in a position to see what answers a 'theoretical' approach gives to the sort of question we have asked in the earlier parts of this book.

If the answers agree you may consider that common sense has been confirmed by theory, or theory by common sense, depending upon your inclination. It is as well, however, not to despise common sense too much, for it often expresses, perhaps in a not very precise way, the results of much previous experience or experimentation. So when theory contradicts your common sense don't automatically think you are stupid—take a cool look at the theory, particularly the assumptions or premises from which it starts. We shall find later a clear case where our common sense gives a more sensible answer than our theory, as well as one showing the opposite.

When we chose the mean, the standard deviation and the standard error as the basic quantities for describing the results of experiments, one of the justifications we used was that these quantities approached limiting values as the number of measurements was indefinitely increased, so that they became characteristics of the limiting frequency distribution curve. This is the origin of our common sense approach, though in no way a proof of its correctness. Our theoretical approach carries this idea somewhat further. It assumes that any experiment not only has a probability distribution curve for yielding a range of measurements, but that this curve has a definite form (for example, one of those discussed in Chapter 5) and that the measurements actually made are a random sample of those to be expected from this particular distribution. This then enables us to give numerical criteria for deciding which is the best distribution, for describing our confidence in the truth of a prediction or hypothesis, and for discussing other allied topics.

6.1   MAXIMUM LIKELIHOOD—GAUSSIAN DISTRIBUTION

To see how this works, let us look again at Robinson's measurements (1.52, 1.50, 1.51, 1.53, 1.51 sec). Suppose we now assume that the true value is, say, 1.54 sec and that the apparatus is such as to give a Gaussian distribution of measurements with a precision determined by the standard deviation 0.02 sec. The distribution of Robinson's measurements should then follow the law

$$f(x) = \frac{1}{(2\pi)^{\frac{1}{2}} \times 0.02} \exp\left[-\frac{(x-1.54)^2}{2 \times (0.02)^2}\right].$$

This gives, for the five measurements $x_1 = 1.53$, $x_2 = 1.50$, $x_3 = 1.51$, $x_4 = 1.52$, $x_5 = 1.51$ sec, the values $f(x_1) = 17.60$, $f(x_2) = 2.70$, $f(x_3) = 6.48$, $f(x_4) = 12.10$, $f(x_5) = 6.48$.

Hence the likelihood, or probability that Robinson would make the five measurements that he did in fact make, is proportional to

$$P_1 = f(x_1)f(x_2)f(x_3)f(x_4)f(x_5) = 2.41 \times 10^4.$$

If, instead, we choose the values calculated in section 2.7,

$$X = 1.514 \text{ sec}, \qquad \sigma = 0.010 \text{ sec},$$

to define the Gaussian curve, the probability of the five results occurring is proportional to

$$P_{\text{II}} = 7.50 \times 10^6.$$

So this second choice gives a greater likelihood for the observed results to occur and is in this sense, the better choice. What, then, is the *best* choice; that is, the one that gives the *maximum likelihood*?

To answer this we shall consider the general case of measurements $x_1, x_2, \ldots, x_n$ which are assumed to be a random sample arising from a Gaussian probability curve

$$f(x) = \frac{1}{(2\pi)^{\frac{1}{2}}\sigma} \exp\left[-\frac{(x-X)^2}{2\sigma^2}\right].$$

The overall probability of observing $x_1, x_2, \ldots, x_n$ is then proportional to

$$P = f(x_1)f(x_2)\ldots f(x_n)$$

$$= \frac{1}{(2\pi)^{n/2}\sigma^n}\exp\left\{-\frac{1}{2\sigma^2}[(x_1-X)^2 + (x_2-X)^2+\ldots+(x_n-X)^2]\right\}.$$

Now P depends upon both X, the assumed true value, and σ, the assumed standard deviation, so that by varying these we may hope to reach its maximum value, when

$$\partial P/\partial X = 0 \quad \text{and} \quad \partial P/\partial\sigma = 0.$$

When P is a maximum $S = \log P$ will be also, and it is simpler algebraically to find

$$\partial S/\partial X = 0 \quad \text{and} \quad \partial S/\partial\sigma = 0,$$

where

$$S = \log P = -n \log (2\pi)/2 - n \log \sigma - [(x_1-X)^2 + (x_2-X)^2 + \ldots + (x_n-X)^2]/(2\sigma^2).$$

Then

$$\partial S/\partial X = [(x_1-X)+(x_2-X)+\ldots+(x_n-X)]/\sigma^2$$
$$= [(x_1+x_2+\ldots+x_n) - nX]/\sigma^2$$

and

$$\partial S/\partial\sigma = -n/\sigma + [(x_1-X)^2 + (x_2-X)^2 + \ldots + (x_n-X)^2]/\sigma^3$$
$$= [(x_1-X)^2 + (x_2-X)^2 + \ldots + (x_n-X)^2 - n\sigma^2]/\sigma^3.$$

So S, and therefore P, are at their maxima (it is straightforward to show they are maxima and not minima) when the true value is taken to be

$$X = (x_1+x_2+\ldots+x_n)/n = X_n \tag{6.1}$$

and the standard deviation to be

$$\sigma = [(x_1-X)^2 + (x_2-X)^2 + \ldots + (x_n-X)^2]^{\frac{1}{2}}/n^{\frac{1}{2}} = \sigma_n. \tag{6.2}$$

So this approach agrees with our earlier one in choosing the arithmetic mean as the best estimate of the true value. It differs from it in the best estimate of the standard deviation by having the factor $n^{-\frac{1}{2}}$ instead of $(n-1)^{-\frac{1}{2}}$. This difference shows up most clearly when $n = 1$. We decide earlier that no estimate of precision was possible in this case, whereas we now appear to have $\sigma = 0$ as the best estimate.

Common sense wins here for it still remains true that from one measurement *alone* two distinct deductions cannot be made. To discuss fully the significance of the two different approaches is not within the scope of this book, but it is worth pointing out why we should expect this maximum likelihood approach to give strange answers when $n = 1$.

Firstly, for the value $\sigma = 0$ neither the Gaussian curve, nor $\partial S/\partial X$ nor $\partial S/\partial \sigma$ are defined since they include respectively the factors σ^{-1}, σ^{-2} and σ^{-3}. We should strictly consider the limiting values as $\sigma \to 0$. Secondly, the expressions $f(x_1), f(x_2), \ldots$ are only proportional to the probabilities of observing $x_1, x_2, \ldots$ in a limited sense. We should have said that $f(x_1)\, dx$ is the probability of observing a measurement in a small interval dx enclosing the value x_1, with a similar qualification for $f(x_2), f(x_3)$, and the rest. This would have dealt with the fact that the values of $f(x)$ we calculated above were all greater than unity, whereas a true probability cannot exceed unity. However, provided that dx is so small compared with σ that the variation of $f(x)$ over the intervals dx is negligible, this wordiness is rather tiresome, since the intervals remain as constants in the equations and are not affected by the differentiation involved in the maximum likelihood derivation.

Nevertheless, when the calculated value of σ is itself small it may not be physically meaningful to assume that dx is much smaller still. For example, the fact that Robinson gives his results to two decimal places must imply that a measurement such as 1.52 sec does not mean 1.520000 . . . sec but rather that it lies, say, between 1.515 and 1.525 sec. The probability of observing this would strictly be

$$P(1.52) = \int_{1.515}^{1.525} f(x)\, dx$$

and the approximation,

$$P(1.52) = f(1.52) \times 0.01,$$

which is implicit in our earlier argument, is satisfactory only if $f(x)$ varies very little over the interval (1.515, 1.525). Clearly this is not true of the Gaussian curve once σ becomes comparable with 0.01, and we should be in considerable error in using the approximate value throughout the limiting process $\sigma \to 0$.

There is a deeper reason for doubling the maximum likelihood answer when n is small. Equations 6.1 and 6.2 are derived on the assumption that the measurements are a sample of a Gaussian distribution. In other words we are saying that if we are *certain* that the Gaussian distribution applies, then we may use these equations. But, of course, we are never certain of this, least of all when there is only one measurement. Consequently any estimating of the shape of the Gaussian curve ought to include a factor that takes account of the uncertainty about whether such a curve is in any case appropriate. Clearly the smaller the number of measurements the greater this uncertainty is.

In view of this, and remembering that when n is small the accuracy of estimating σ is poor and that when n is large the difference between $n^{-\frac{1}{2}}$ and $(n-1)^{-\frac{1}{2}}$ is negligible, it is clear that the best estimate of σ.

$$s_n = [(x_1 - X)^2 + (x_2 - X)^2 + \ldots + (x_n - X)^2]^{\frac{1}{2}}/(n-1)^{\frac{1}{2}},$$

which we derived earlier, is not invalidated by the maximum likelihood approach.

Once we have assumed that the n measurements $x_1, x_2, \ldots, x_n$ are a random sample drawn from a Gaussian distribution then we may use the approach of section 2.4 to show that the mean

$$X_n = (x_1 + x_2 + \ldots + x_n)/n$$

is a sample of a Gaussian distribution of standard deviation

$$\sigma(X_n) = n^{-\frac{1}{2}}\sigma.$$

The standard error is then S_n and the best value and its error are

$$X = X_n \pm S_n,$$

where

$$S_n^2 = [(x_1 - X_n)^2 + (x_2 - X_n)^2 + \ldots + (x_n - X_n)^2]/[n(n-1)].$$

6.2 MAXIMUM LIKELIHOOD—POISSON DISTRIBUTION

In a similar way for a set of numbers or counts assumed to be a sample from a Poisson distribution we can determine which Poisson distribution would give the maximum likelihood for their occurrence. If $r_1, r_2, \ldots, r_n$ are observed, the probability of their arising from the distribution

$$P(r; \mu) = e^{-\mu}\mu^r/r!$$

is

$$Q = P(r_1; \mu)P(r_2; \mu) \ldots P(r_n; \mu)$$
$$= \frac{e^{-n\mu}\mu^{r_1+r_2+\ldots+r_n}}{r_1!r_2!\ldots r_n!}.$$

Then

$$S = \log Q = (r_1 + r_2 + \ldots + r_n)\log \mu - n\mu - \log(r_1!r_2!\ldots r_n!).$$

There is only one adjustable parameter, μ, so that S, and therefore Q, will be a maximum when

$$\partial S/\partial \mu = (r_1 + r_2 + \ldots r_n)/\mu - n = 0.$$

Hence the optimum value is

$$\mu = (r_1 + r_2 + \ldots + r_n)/n = R_n, \tag{6.3}$$

the mean value of the n counts.

μ completely fixes the Poisson distribution. The standard deviation, as we have already seen, is $\mu^{\frac{1}{2}}$ and does not therefore need to be calculated separately. We could nevertheless do so, using the experimental counts, and the degree to which this agreed with $R_n^{\frac{1}{2}}$ would be an indication of how well justified we were in assuming the counts to be a sample of a Poisson distribution. For example, the two sets of 10 counts, 9, 9, 9, 9, 9, 9, 9, 9, 9, 9 and 7, 10, 6, 12, 9, 8, 9, 14, 7, 8 both have the same mean value

$$R_n = 9$$

and, therefore, if each arose from a Poisson distribution it would be the same for both,

$$P(r; \mu) = P(r; 9) = e^{-9}9^r/r!.$$

However, the best estimates of the standard deviation calculated in the two cases directly from the observations are

$$\sigma_{nI} = 0$$

and

$$\sigma_{nII} = 2.45,$$

as compared with the expected value

$$\sigma = \mu^{\frac{1}{2}} = 3.$$

It is clear from these figures that the Poisson assumption is a reasonable one for the second set of numbers but is very doubtful for the first. Indeed we would suspect that some deterministic mechanism was responsible for them and that random processes were playing very little part.

6.3 CONFIDENCE

Although the approach based on assumed distributions has so far led to much the same results as we obtained earlier, it gives a much greater depth of understanding of the problems and provides a powerful and consistent method for analysing more complicated situations.

For one thing it gives an exact meaning to describing precision and error in terms of σ and S_n. If x_i is a sample measurement from the Gaussian distribution, we saw in section 5.3 that the probability that it would lie in the interval

$$X - \sigma \le x_i \le X + \sigma$$

is

$$\int_{X-\sigma}^{X+\sigma} P(x; X, \sigma)\, dx = 0.683.$$

We can express this by saying that the limits $\pm\sigma$ give a 68.3% *confidence level* for a single measurement x_i. Similarly the limits $\pm 3\sigma$ give a 99.7% confidence level.

If we know σ it is not so much the confidence in x_i that we require, since this is what we actually observe anyway, but confidence in our estimate of the true value, X. Now the Gaussian distribution,

$$P(x; X, \sigma) = \frac{1}{(2\pi)^{\frac{1}{2}}\sigma} \exp\left[-\frac{(x-X)^2}{2\sigma^2}\right],$$

is of such a form that

$$P(x; X, \sigma) = P(X; x, \sigma).$$

Thus any error, $\varepsilon = x - X$, can be regarded equally well as a displacement of x from X, or of X from x, and the distribution of X's, *relative to the measurements*, would follow a Gaussian distribution with the *same* standard deviation. So a single measurement, x_i, together with the knowledge or assumption that it arises from a Gaussian distribution of standard deviation σ, gives a 68.3% confidence that the true value will be contained within the interval $x_i \pm \sigma$ and a 99.7% confidence within $x_i \pm 3\sigma$.

As it stands this is a result of rather limited application. Firstly, σ must be supplied from some source other than the single measurement, x_i, and, secondly, we in any case do not know that x_i does belong to a Gaussian distribution.

However, when a group of n measurements are available the result has a much greater significance. This is because of the *central limit theorem*—a statistical theorem of great importance. This states that the mean, X_n, of n measurements *does* follow a Gaussian distribution, whatever the distribution of the individual measurements. Moreover, we have already seen that the n measurements themselves provide a best estimate, S_n, of the standard deviation of the mean.

This is by no means a rigorous statement of the theorem. There are some probability distributions for which the mean of n measurements does not follow the Gaussian law. But the range of distributions for which the theorem is true is so wide that it covers most experimental situations. Also, the theorem becomes true only as n increases towards infinity. It is an approximation for large n and is clearly untrue when $n = 1$.

However, with these reservations, we can see that the standard error S_n, which is the best estimate of the standard deviation of the mean of n measurements as we showed in section 2.4, can nearly always be interpreted in terms of confidence levels. A result $X_n \pm S_n$ corresponds to a 68.3% confidence level for the interval $(X_n - S_m, X_n + S_n)$ to contain the true value, X, and $X_n \pm 3S_n$ to a 99.7% confidence level. In practice confidence levels of 99.0% are often used as criteria of acceptance. From Appendix 2 we see that

$$\psi(y) = 0.99$$

when

$$y = 2.58.$$

Hence the 99% confidence level occurs for the limits $X_n \pm 2.58S_n$.

6.4 BEST COMBINED ESTIMATES

As another example of the technique of the maximum likelihood method let us consider how best to combine the measurements $x_1, x_2, \ldots, x_n$ from one experiment with the measurements $x'_1, x'_2, \ldots, x'_m$ from another, when both experiments are attempting to find the true value X. Our starting assumption is that the first n results are a random sample arising from a distribution

$$f(x) = \frac{1}{(2\pi)^{\frac{1}{2}}\sigma} \exp\left[-\frac{(x-X)^2}{2\sigma^2}\right]$$

and the second m results are from a distribution

$$f'(x) = \frac{1}{(2\pi)^{\frac{1}{2}}\sigma'} \exp\left[-\frac{(x-X)^2}{2\sigma'^2}\right].$$

X will, of course, be the same for both distributions since both experiments are measuring the same quantity, but there may be different values, σ and σ', for the precision of the two sets of apparatus.

Then the probability of obtaining the two sets of results is proportional to

$$P = f(x_1)f(x_2)\ldots f(x_n)f'(x_1')f'(x_2')\ldots f'(x_m').$$

We wish to maximize this, or, more conveniently,

$$S = \log P$$

by choosing optimum values for X, σ and σ'. The conditions

$$\partial S/\partial X = 0, \qquad \partial S/\partial\sigma = 0, \qquad \partial S/\partial\sigma' = 0,$$

give respectively,

$$\sigma^{-2}[(x_1+x_2+\ldots+x_n)-nX]+\sigma'^{-2}[(x_1'+x_2'+\ldots+x_m')-mX] = 0,$$

$$\sigma^{-3}[(x_1-X)^2+(x_2-X)^2+\ldots+(x_n-X)^2-n\sigma^2] = 0,$$

$$\sigma'^{-3}[(x_1'-X)^2+(x_2'-X)^2+\ldots+(x_m'-X)^2-m\sigma'^2] = 0,$$

or, since

$$nX_n = x_1+x_2+\ldots+x_n$$

and

$$mX_m' = x_1'+x_2'+\ldots+x_m',$$

then

$$n\sigma^{-2}(X_n-X)+m\sigma'^{-2}(X_m'-X) = 0, \qquad (6.4)$$

$$(x_1-X_n)^2+\ldots+(x_n-X_n)^2+n(X_n-X)^2-n\sigma^2 = 0, \qquad (6.5)$$

$$(x_1'-X_m')^2+\ldots+(x_m'-X_m')^2+m(X_m'-X)^2-m\sigma'^2 = 0, \qquad (6.6)$$

assuming

$$\sigma \neq 0, \qquad \sigma' \neq 0.$$

For the two experiments considered separately we would define the mean square deviations, σ_n^2 and $\sigma_m'^2$, by the equations

$$n\sigma_n^2 = (x_1 - X_n)^2 + \ldots + (x_n - X_n)^2$$
$$m\sigma_m'^2 = (X_1' - X_m')^2 + \ldots + (x_m' - X_m')^2,$$

so we may rewrite Equations 6.5 and 6.6 as

$$\sigma^2 = \sigma_n^2 + (X_n - X)^2, \tag{6.7}$$

$$\sigma'^2 = \sigma_m'^2 + (X_m' - X)^2. \tag{6.8}$$

From Equations 6.4, 6.7 and 6.8 we have, finally,

$$n(X_n - X)[\sigma_m'^2 + (X_m' - X)^2] + m(X_m' - X)[\sigma_n^2 + (X_n - X)^2] = 0 \tag{6.9}$$

This is a cubic equation for X, whose general solution is rather complicated and will not be attempted here. Its character depends markedly upon the relative values of n and m, and of σ_n^2, $\sigma_m'^2$ and $(X_n - X_m')^2$. If we take a few special cases we shall see that this theoretical approach reveals aspects of the problem which our earlier common sense overlooked.

6.4.1 Consistent experiments

Suppose the separation of the two estimates, $|X_n - X_m'|$, is rather smaller than either standard deviation σ_n, σ_m'. Then, since X lies between X_n and X_m',

$$(X_n - X)^2 \ll \sigma_n^2 \quad \text{and} \quad (X_m' - X)^2 \ll \sigma_m'^2.$$

Neglecting the small quantities entirely, Equation 6.9 reduces to

$$n(X_n - X)\sigma_m'^2 + m(X_m' - X)\sigma_n^2 = 0.$$

Then, neglecting also the differences between n and $n-1$, and between m and $m-1$, we may write

$$S_n^2 = \sigma_n^2/n, \qquad S_m'^2 = \sigma_m'^2/m$$

and obtain the approximate solution

$$X = \frac{1}{S_n^{-2} + S_m'^{-2}} \left(\frac{X_n}{S_n^2} + \frac{X_m'}{S_m'^2} \right).$$

If this is used as the starting point for a second approximation it can be shown that

$$X = \frac{S_n^2 S_m'^2}{S_n^2 + S_m'^2}\left(\frac{X_n}{S_n^2} + \frac{X_m'}{S_m'^2}\right) + \frac{S_n^2 S_m'^2 (S_n^2 - S_m'^2)}{(S_n^2 + S_m'^2)^4}(X_n - X_m')^3. \quad (6.10)$$

From Equations 6.7 and 6.8 we have the maximum likelihood estimates of the standard deviations of the two experiments and consequently of their standard errors σ^2/n and σ'^2/m. Using these to estimate the error of the combined result as given by Equation 6.10, we can show that the standard error, $S_{n,m}$, has for its second approximation,

$$S_{n,m}^{-2} = S_n^{-2} + S_m'^{-2} - \left(\frac{X_n - X_m'}{S_m^2 + S_m'^2}\right)^2\left(\frac{1}{n} + \frac{1}{m}\right). \quad (6.11)$$

We see that the leading terms in Equations 6.10 and 6.11 are the same as those obtained in section 3.5. In both cases the additional terms increase in magnitude as the separation between the two means becomes comparable with the separate standard deviations. In the case of Equation 6.11 the term is always negative and represents an increase in overall error. On reflection we can see that this is a very reasonable result—two estimates which are close together must give a more accurate joint value than they would when farther apart, even though the separately estimated standard deviations remain unchanged.

Of course, if they are really far apart, that is, compared with their separately estimated standard deviations, neither of the approximations (6.10) and (6.11) will apply.

6.4.2   Inconsistent experiments

By inconsistent we really mean any results which do not satisfy the requirements of section 6.4.1. Thus if $|X_n - X_m'|$ were rather greater than either σ_n or σ_m' the preceding results would not hold and we should have to return to the complete Equation 6.9. However, to simplify the algebra we will take an extreme and special case

$$(X_n - X_m')^2 \gg \sigma_n^2 \simeq \sigma_m'^2, \qquad m = n,$$

that is, two experiments of nearly equal precision, with equal numbers of measurements from each, whose estimates of the true value differ by at least several times their standard deviations. If the two standard deviations were exactly the same the two experiments would be alike in every respect and on grounds of symmetry alone we would expect for their joint estimate the central value

$$X = (X_n + X'_n)/2,$$

as may readily be checked from Equation 6.9.

Using this as a first approximation, the second approximation for Equation 6.9 is

$$X = \frac{X_n - X'_n}{2}\left[1 - \frac{2(\sigma_n^2 - \sigma'^2_n)}{X_n^2 - X'^2_n}\right]. \tag{6.12}$$

The maximum likelihood estimates of precision, σ, σ', (Equations 6.7 and 6.8) now differ considerably from those estimated separately by the experiments, σ_n, σ'_n. The combined standard error, $S_{n,n}$, using these revised values, is given by

$$S_{n,n}^2 = (X_n - X'_n)^2/(8n) + (S_n^2 + S'^2_n)/4. \tag{6.13}$$

The first terms of Equations 6.12 and 6.13 would be obtained by lumping together all the n measurements from the one experiment at the value X_n, and those from the other at X'_n. Here the joint error is determined almost entirely by the separation of the two estimates. What the result does, in effect, is to reject the original estimates of precision and error and substitute for them much larger ones. This is why we call the results inconsistent—it is very unlikely that the separate estimates of the true value *and* standard errors are correct, in other words the likelihood of all four quantities resulting from random error distributions is very small.

If we insist that random errors only are responsible for inconsistent results, then one at least of the numbers X_n, X'_m, σ_n, σ'_m will need considerable revision as the best estimate of the quantity it purports to measure. But when such a situation arises it is worth considering whether one, or both, of the experiments has undisclosed sources of systematic error. For if results from an experiment are grouped closely about a value X_n they will be distributed approximately according to, say, a Gaussian form as in figure 6.1.

If, as a result of combining these results with others, a much wider distribution with different mean turns out to give the maximum combined likelihood it is clear from the figure that the observed distribution is very far from an approximation to this new distribution. If the number of measurements is large the hypothesis that they are a sample of the new distribution becomes highly doubtful and the careful experimentalist will look around for alternative credible hypotheses which would fit the results better.

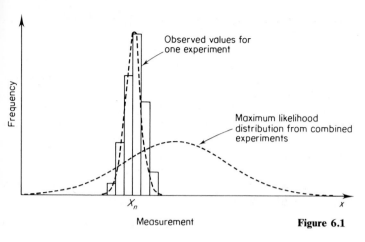

Observed values for
one experiment

Maximum likelihood
distribution from combined
experiments

X_n

Measurement

Figure 6.1

A systematic error is one such possibility. Or it may be that the
two quantities apparently the same are in reality different.

6.5   TRUTH OF A HYPOTHESIS: THE χ^2 TEST

It should be remembered that since, for any continuous distribution, $f(x)\,dx$ is the probability of obtaining a value in the interval
dx, then the probability of obtaining any particular result, x, is
strictly zero, for this requires $dx = 0$. In this sense no single value
of x is more likely than any other. Nevertheless, all measurements
do *not* have the same standing when we are trying to find out
whether $f(x)$ truly represents the experimental situation. It is clear
that one measurement near the peak of $f(x)$ gives more support or
backing for the truth of $f(x)$ than one several standard deviations
away.

Can we express this quantitatively without using some implied
value of dx? We can, by asking the question, how likely are we to
obtain a result worse than the one under consideration? We obtain
a precise answer if we define worse to mean *possessing a smaller
likelihood*.

Thus

$$x \text{ is worse than } x_0$$

if

$$f(x) < f(x_0). \tag{6.14}$$

Then, if $f(x)$ truly represents the frequency distribution of measurements, the probability of obtaining any value worse than x_0 is

$$B(x_0) = \int f(x) \, dx, \qquad (6.15)$$

where this integral is taken over all the values of x to which the inequality 6.14 applies. $B(x_0)$ we shall call the *backing* of x_0, where this means the backing of x_0 *for* a particular assumption or hypothesis. It is, of course, not a function simply of x_0, but depends upon x_0 and the assumed frequency distribution and could be written more fully as $B[x_0; f(x)]$. However, in what follows it is clear what the assumption is, and the shorter form will suffice.

If $f(x)$ is a single peaked curve (figure 6.2)

$$B(x_0) = \int_{-\infty}^{y_0} f(x) \, dx + \int_{x_0}^{\infty} f(x) \, dx,$$

and if, in addition, it is symmetrical (figure 6.3)

$$B(x_0) = 2 \int_{x_0}^{\infty} f(x) \, dx.$$

In the symmetrical case a measurement that is worse than x_0 simply means one that is further from the true value, X.

Qualitatively $B(x_0)$ has the properties we should expect. When $x_0 = X$, the assumed true value, then $B(x_0) = 1$. This maximum value is the greatest support that a single measurement can give to the hypothesis. As x_0 moves away from X, $B(x_0)$ decreases towards zero, rapidly if the distribution is narrow, slowly if it is wide. A value for x_0 well outside the peak of the assumed distribution gives it very little support.

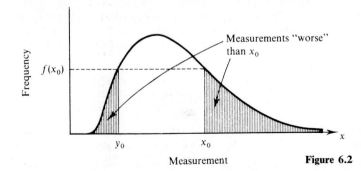

Measurements "worse" than x_0

$f(x_0)$

y_0 x_0 x

Measurement   **Figure 6.2**

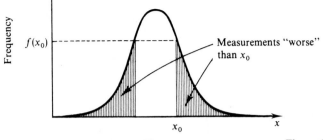

Figure 6.3

When the assumed distribution is Gaussian,

$$P(x; X, \sigma) = \frac{1}{(2\pi)^{\frac{1}{2}}\sigma} \exp\left[-\frac{(x-X)^2}{2\sigma^2}\right],$$

the backing of x_0 is

$$B(x_0) = 2\int_{x_0}^{\infty} P(x; X, \sigma)\, dx$$

$$= \left(\frac{2}{\pi}\right)^{\frac{1}{2}} \int_{\chi}^{\infty} \exp\left(-\kappa^2/2\right) d\kappa$$

$$= 1 - \psi(\chi), \tag{6.16}$$

where

$$\kappa = (x - X)/\sigma, \qquad \chi = (x_0 - X)/\sigma,$$

and where $\psi(\chi)$ is defined by Equation 5.14 and is tabulated in Appendix 2.

Suppose now that we have two independent measurements, x', x'', perhaps of two quite different quantities, for each of which a separate Gaussian distribution is proposed:

$$P(x'; X', \sigma') = \frac{1}{(2\pi)^{\frac{1}{2}}\sigma'} \exp\left[-\frac{(x'-X')^2}{2\sigma'^2}\right],$$

$$P(x''; X'', \sigma'') = \frac{1}{(2\pi)^{\frac{1}{2}}\sigma''} \exp\left[-\frac{(x''-X'')^2}{2\sigma''^2}\right].$$

Any pair of measurements, x', x'', will be worse than an observed pair, x_0', x_0'', if their combined likelihood is worse, that is, if

$$P(x'; X', \sigma')P(x''; X'', \sigma'') < P(x_0'; X', \sigma')P(x_0''; X'', \sigma'').$$

Now

$$P(x'; X', \sigma')P(x''; X'', \sigma'') = \frac{1}{2\pi\sigma'\sigma''} \exp\left(-\frac{\kappa'^2 + \kappa''^2}{2}\right)$$

and

$$P(x_0'; X', \sigma')P(x_0''; X'', \sigma'') = \frac{1}{2\pi\sigma'\sigma''} \exp\left(-\frac{\kappa_0'^2 + \kappa_0''^2}{2}\right),$$

where

$$\kappa' = (x' - X')/\sigma', \qquad \kappa'' = (x'' - X'')/\sigma'',$$
$$\kappa_0' = (x_0' - X')/\sigma', \qquad \kappa_0'' = (x_0'' - X'')/\sigma''.$$

Hence x', x'' will be worse than x_0', x_0'' if

$$\kappa'^2 + \kappa''^2 > \kappa_0'^2 + \kappa_0''^2 = \chi^2,$$

say, and the backing of x_0', x_0'' for the assumed double Gaussian distribution will be

$$B(x_0', x_0'') = \frac{1}{2\pi} \iint \exp\left(-\frac{\kappa'^2 + \kappa''^2}{2}\right) d\kappa' \, d\kappa'',$$

where the integration is over all κ', κ'' satisfying

$$\kappa'^2 + \kappa''^2 > \chi^2.$$

In a similar way if n measurements, $x_0', x_0'', \ldots, x_0^{(n)}$ are recorded and Gaussian distributions are proposed for them with true values $X', X'', \ldots, X^{(n)}$ and standard deviations $\sigma', \sigma'', \ldots, \sigma^{(n)}$, we can define

$$\chi^2 = \kappa_0'^2 + \kappa_0''^2 + \ldots + \kappa_0^{(n)2}$$
$$= (x_0' - X')^2/\sigma'^2 + (x_0'' - X'')^2/\sigma''^2 + \ldots + (x_0^{(n)} - X^{(n)})^2/\sigma^{(n)2}$$

and the backing is then

$$B(x_0', x_0'', \ldots, x_0^{(n)}) = \left(\frac{1}{2\pi}\right)^{n/2} \iint_{\kappa'^2 + \kappa''^2 + \ldots + \kappa^{(n)2} > \chi^2} \cdots \int \exp\left[-(\kappa'^2 + \kappa''^2 + \ldots \right.$$

$$\left. + \kappa^{(n)2})/2\right] d\kappa' \, d\kappa'' \ldots d\kappa^{(n)}. \qquad (6.17)$$

This backing is determined by n, the number of independent measurements, and by χ, and it is therefore usual to write it as

$$P_n(>\chi^2) = B(x_0', x_0'', \ldots, x_0^{(n)}).$$

Moreover, the multiple integral can be reduced to a single one, to give in place of Equation 6.17

$$P_n(>\chi^2) = \frac{1}{2^{(n-2)/2}[(n-2)/2]!} \int_\chi^\infty \kappa^{n-1} e^{-\kappa^2/2} \, d\kappa, \qquad (6.18)$$

where

$$\left(\frac{n-2}{2}\right)! = \frac{n-2}{2} \times \frac{n-4}{2} \times \ldots \times 2 \times 1$$

when n is even, and

$$\left(\frac{n-2}{2}\right)! = \frac{n-2}{2} \times \frac{n-4}{2} \times \ldots \times \frac{3}{2} \times \frac{1}{2} \times \pi^{\frac{1}{2}}$$

when n is odd.

Values of $P_{n'}(>\chi^2)$ are given in Appendix 4. n' is used rather than n for a reason that will be explained shortly. The first row simply repeats information given by the integral Gaussian probability for a single measurement. Thus $\chi^2 = 2$ or $\chi = 1.414$ gives a backing of 0.1575 or 15.8% and we obtain from Appendix 2, by interpolation, the equivalent result—that the probability of obtaining a value y *outside* the limits ± 1.414 is $1.0000 - 0.8426 = 0.1574$.

Two such measurements would give $\chi^2 = 4$ and a backing, from the second column of Appendix 4 ($n' = 2$), of 13.5%.

Frequently it is not n separate distributions that are to be tested by the backing that $x_0', x_0'', \ldots, x_0^{(n)}$ give them, but a single distribution $P(x; \alpha, \beta, \ldots)$ depending upon one or more parameters $\alpha, \beta, \ldots$ which fix its position and shape. Suppose interval end points $x_0, x_1, \ldots, x_m$ are decided upon, so that the probability of obtaining a measurement x in (x_{i-1}, x_i) is

$$p_i = \int_{x_{i-1}}^{x_i} P(x; \alpha, \beta, \ldots) \, dx.$$

Then, of the n measurements made we should expect np_i to fall within this interval. Now if we regard the np_i as an average count arising from a random process we know from section 5.4 that the counts actually observed should fluctuate about np_i with standard deviation $(np_i)^{\frac{1}{2}}$ and that if $np_i \gtrsim 10$ their distribution will be approximately Gaussian. Consequently we have, in effect, to find the backing that the n measurements give to m separate Gaussian distributions with peaks at $np_1, np_2, \ldots, np_m$ and standard deviations $(np_1)^{\frac{1}{2}}, (np_2)^{\frac{1}{2}}, \ldots, (np_m)^{\frac{1}{2}}$.

If the numbers of measurements in the intervals are actually $n_1, n_2, \ldots, n_m$, these give the value

$$\chi^2 = \kappa_0'^2 + \kappa_0''^2 + \ldots + \kappa_0^{(m)2}$$
$$= (n_1 - np_1)^2/np_1 + (n_2 - np_2)^2/np_2 + \ldots + (n_m - np_m)^2/np_m \tag{6.19}$$

and a backing $P_m(>\chi^2)$.

However, this is not the whole story. Just as the criterion (6.14) compares the single measurement made with any other possible *single* measurement, so the general result (6.18) is derived by comparing the n measurements made with any other possible group of measurements *also n in number*. Therefore, if $\nu_1, \nu_2, \ldots, \nu_m$ are the numbers in each interval from another such group, we must have

$$\nu_1 + \nu_2 + \ldots + \nu_m = n = n_1 + n_2 + \ldots + n_m,$$

from which it is simple to show that the corresponding κ's are constrained to satisfy the linear relationship,

$$p_1^{\frac{1}{2}}\kappa' + p_2^{\frac{1}{2}}\kappa'' + \ldots + p_m^{\frac{1}{2}}\kappa^{(m)} = 0 = p_1^{\frac{1}{2}}\kappa_0' + p_2^{\frac{1}{2}}\kappa_0'' + \ldots + p_m^{\frac{1}{2}}\kappa_0^{(m)}. \tag{6.20}$$

Hence only $m-1$ of the κ's are independent and the backing becomes $P_{m-1}(>\chi^2)$. There may be further restrictions. For example, one of the parameters of the distribution—the true value, X—is often determined as the mean of the measurements made. If so, there will be only $m-2$ independent κ's and the appropriate backing will be $P_{m-2}(>\chi^2)$.

In general there may be l *constraints* which reduce the original m *degrees of freedom* to

[See §6.7.1, page 135; §6.7.2, page 136]

$$n' = m - l, \tag{6.21}$$

and the backing, based on the χ^2 test (*chi squared test*) becomes $P_{n'}(>\chi^2)$.

6.6   RETURN OF JENKINS AND ROBINSON

Finally, what of Jenkins and Robinson, whose opposing views set off our discussion, and whom we have rather forgotten since the end of Chapter 3? Most of the calculation has been done, but the interpretation can now be extended.

Jenkins' result (1.533 ± 0.007) sec implies, if it is assumed that his mean is a sample of a Gaussian distribution, that at the 68.3% confidence level the interval $(1.526, 1.540)$ sec will contain the true value (section 6.3). For 99% confidence the interval is $(1.514, 1.552)$ sec. For Robinson's result (1.514 ± 0.005) sec the interval for 68.3% is $(1.509, 1.519)$ sec and for 99% is $(1.501, 1.527)$ sec. We note that the two larger intervals overlap in the common interval $(1.514, 1.527)$ sec, so that for the true value to be in this interval would not make either result an extremely unlikely one.

The least squares combined result (1.520 ± 0.004) can be recalculated as a maximum likelihood estimate (section 6.4.1), though with some reservations about the accuracy of Equation 6.10, since the best estimate of σ for Robinson's apparatus ($s_n = 0.010$ sec—section 2.7) is rather smaller than the difference between his and Jenkins' result $(1.533 - 1.514 = 0.019$ sec). This changes the result to (1.525 ± 0.005) sec (significance 0.001)—a barely appreciable change in the overall accuracy, but a significant alteration in the estimated true value.

This is about as far as it is worth pursuing the analysis. In principle we could discuss, in the manner of section 6.5, the backing the results give to the assumptions underlying the maximum likelihood estimates. Jenkins' 500 measurements could certainly be examined in this way. But Robinson made only 5, and this is too small for a statistical test to have any great significance. If we suspect that, since the difference between Robinson's estimate and the combined maximum likelihood estimate—0.011 sec—exceeds twice his estimated standard error, there may be a systematic error in one or both experiments, the best course would be to examine the details of the experiments and see what precautions were taken to avoid such errors. If doubt still remains we return appropriately to the golden rule of Chapter 1 and ask Robinson to make more measurements!

6.7   COMMENTS AND WORKED EXAMPLE

6.7.1   Example 18 (See page 134)

Compare the following cosmic ray counts over 100 separate hours as evidence of Poisson distributions:

No. of counts		≤ 2	3	4	5	6	7	8	9	10	11	12	13	14	15	16	17	≥ 18
No. of hours	A	0	1	2	4	7	8	10	12	14	11	10	6	7	4	2	2	0
	B	-	-	-	-	-	-	0	0	100	0	0	-	-	-	-	-	-

The mean of both A and B counts is $10 \, \mathrm{hr}^{-1}$. From Appendix 3 we calculate the following:

No. of counts	Expected No. of hours	Observed No. of hours		Deviations $\delta_i = n_i - np_i$		$\kappa^{(i)2} = \delta_i^2/np_i$	
		A	B	A	B	A	B
≤ 6	13.0	14	0	+1.0	−13.0	0.769	13.0
7, 8	20.3	18	0	−2.3	−20.3	0.261	20.3
9, 10	25.0	26	100	+1.0	+75.0	0.040	225.0
11, 12	20.9	21	0	+0.1	−20.9	0.000	20.9
≥ 13	20.8	21	0	+0.2	−20.8	0.002	20.8

Hence for results A

$$\chi^2 = \Sigma\kappa^2 = 1.07$$

and for results B

$$\chi^2 = \Sigma\kappa^2 = 300.0.$$

We have divided the categories into 5 (to provide expected numbers rather greater than 10) so that there are 5κ's. These initial 5 degrees of freedom must be reduced by 2 (one for the fixed number of hours and one because the mean is calculated from the results). So we look up the column $n' = 3$ in Appendix 4, which shows that for $\chi^2 = 1.07$ the backing is $P_3(>1.07) \simeq 0.8$, while for $\chi^2 = 300$ the value is well below the bottom of the table, $P_3(>300) \ll 0.0001$.

Results A therefore strongly support a Poisson distribution hypothesis; results B show that it is very unlikely to be true.

6.7.2 (See page 134)

It cannot be emphasized too strongly that the backing is simply a *measure* of support, and that *by itself* it cannot say whether a hypothesis is true or not. Its usefulness lies in giving a quantitative answer so that we can, if the test gives a very low backing for a particular hypothesis, examine the arguments that led to its proposal and see whether there might be alternatives. If there are two or more hypotheses proposed, the test can indicate which is best.

However, even then such preference is only statistical and could be outweighed by other considerations of credibility. For example, suppose two hypotheses were considered in connection with the cosmic ray counts B of the preceding example. One says that as a result of random processes in galactic space a flux of particles strikes the earth showing fluctuations in accord with the Poisson distribution. The other says that a being from Mars is sitting in a spaceship somewhere outside our atmosphere, firing particles at us from a cosmic ray gun at a uniform rate which pass, without interaction, through the atmosphere. From the measurements this rate would be $10\,\text{hr}^{-1}$ and it needs no calculation to show that this hypothesis fits the observations very well. The backing is 1.00—a perfect fit! The first hypothesis we evaluated in section 6.7.1 and achieved an extremely low backing—$\ll 0.0001$.

Do we then believe the Mars spaceship theory and reject the galactic origin? Obviously not, unless we have a great deal more evidence of various kinds to support it. What we should do first is to examine the counting apparatus and see whether deficiencies in it are not a more credible explanation of the uniform counting rate.

Statistics—quantitative results from the analysis of probabilities—are a valuable and essential part of experimental science. But once the statistics have been extracted from an experiment, this is no reason for throwing every other consideration out of the window.

6.8 PROBLEMS

40. Fifteen measurements of a radar wavelength have a mean 3.20 cm and a r.m.s. deviation 0.06 cm. What limits correspond to a 99% confidence level for the true value?

41. What are the limits at the 90% and 99% confidence level for the Poisson distribution with a mean of 7?

42. Each pupil of a class of 28, all assumed equally reliable, measured the concentration of copper sulphate in a given solution. The mean and r.m.s. deviations were $52.2\,\text{g l}^{-1}$ and $1.5\,\text{g l}^{-1}$. Another class of 35 obtained the results $53.1\,\text{g l}^{-1}$ and $2.5\,\text{g l}^{-1}$. Calculate the least squares best estimates of the true value and error from the combined results. What corrections to these does the maximum likelihood method give?

43. One experiment to measure X gives a mean value X_n, and r.m.s. deviation σ_n, from n measurements. A second experiment gives X_m and σ_m from m measurements. If $|X_n - X_m|$ is markedly larger than either σ_n or σ_m, show that the maximum likelihood combined estimate of the true value is approximately the mean of n measurements X_n, and m measurements X_m, all accorded equal weight. What revised estimates of the standard deviation for each experiment will this give, and what error for the estimated true value?

44. Twenty measurements of the wavelength of a spectral line all lie within the interval (4115,4132) Å. Twenty-five measurements of the same line, using different apparatus lie within (4135, 4165) Å. Use the results of Problem 43 to calculate the combined best estimates of the wavelength, the associated error and the standard deviation for each method.

45. If a backing of 1% is taken as the minimum for accepting a hypothesis, do you believe that the two experiments of Problem 44 can be described by two Gaussian distributions with the common mean and standard deviations calculated in that problem?

46. Calculate the means and standard deviations of the 100 and 200 measurements given in Problem 6 (page 25). Evaluate the backing that each set gives for a Gaussian distribution with the same mean and standard deviation (remembering that, since the two parameters of the distribution are determined from the measurements, this introduces two extra constraints). Contrast this support for the existence of a single light (A's hypothesis) with the backing for the following explanation (B's hypothesis):

a) There is one light in the direction 10.75° and another at 11.12°.

b) The sighting apparatus has a precision given by $\sigma = 0.1°$ for observing either light.

c) The light in the direction 11.12° flashes twice as often as the other.

Summary

NOTATION

Simpler alternatives are used if no confusion is likely.

r.m.s. $\equiv$ root mean square.

$\displaystyle\sum_{i=1}^{n} x_i \equiv \Sigma x_i \equiv \Sigma x$ — summation over (n) measured values of x.

$X_n \equiv \bar{x} = \Sigma x/n$ — mean of (n) measured values of x.

X — mean of infinite number of measured values of x; true value of x.

$\delta_i = x_i - X_n$ — deviation of ith measurement from mean.

$\varepsilon_i = x_i - X$ — error of ith measurement or deviation from true value.

$\sigma_n(x) \equiv \sigma_n = (\Sigma \delta^2/n)^{\frac{1}{2}}$ — r.m.s. deviation of x.

$\sigma(x) \equiv \sigma$ — standard deviation of x; precision.

$s_n(x) \equiv s_n = n^{\frac{1}{2}}\sigma_n/(n-1)^{\frac{1}{2}}$ — adjusted r.m.s. deviation of x; best estimate of precision.

$\sigma(X_n)$ — standard deviation of X_n; standard error.

$S_n(x) \equiv S_n = s_n/n^{\frac{1}{2}}$ — adjusted error; best estimate of standard error.

$\sigma_{nm...}(z)$
$s_{nm...}(z)$
$S_{nm...}(z)$ — as above when z is derived from n measurements of x, m of y, ...

$X_{n,m...}$
$S_{n,m...}$ — best combined estimate of true value and standard error from experiments with $n, m, \ldots$ measurements of same quantity.

$_nC_r \equiv \binom{n}{r}$	number of combinations of n, r at a time.
$f(z)$	distribution function for z.
$P(z; \alpha, \beta, \ldots)$ $Q(z; \alpha, \beta, \ldots)$	distribution functions for x, determined by $\alpha, \beta, \ldots$.
$P(x; X, \sigma)$	Gaussian distribution; mean X, standard deviation σ.
$\phi(y)$	standard form of Gaussian distribution.
$\psi(y)$	integral form of Gaussian probability.
$P(r; \mu)$	Poisson distribution; mean μ.
$B[x_0, y_0, \ldots ; f_1(x),$ $f_2(y), \ldots]$ $\equiv B(x_0, y_0, \ldots)$	backing of $x_0, y_0, \ldots$ for distribution function hypotheses $f_1(x), f_2(y), \ldots$.
$P_{n'}(>\chi^2)$	backing based on χ^2 test, with n' degrees of freedom.

CHAPTER 1. Introduction

In order to judge the reliability of an experiment the measurements should be repeated, preferably many times. The results may be presented as normalized frequency distributions. n measurements of x can be shown as a

Discrete distribution: $f_n(x_i)$ is the fraction with $x = x_i$;

or

Histogram: $(x_i - x_{i-1})f_n(x_i)$ is the fraction with $x_{i-1} < x \leq x_i$;

or

Continuous distribution: $\int_{x_\alpha}^{x_\beta} F_n(x)\, dx$ is the fraction with

$$x_\alpha < x \leq x_\beta.$$

Normalization condition is

$$\sum_i f_n(x_i) = \sum_i (x_i - x_{i-1})f_n(x_i) = \int_{-\infty}^{\infty} F_n(x)\, dx = 1 \qquad \begin{matrix}(1.3)\\(1.4)\\(1.5)\end{matrix}$$

Omitting the suffix, n, corresponds to the infinite experiment

$(n \to \infty)$, which defines the true value, X, as the mean

$$X = \bar{x} = \sum_i x_i f(x_i) = \tfrac{1}{2} \sum_i (x_i^2 - x_{i-1}^2) f(x_i) = \int_{-\infty}^{\infty} xF(x)\, dx.$$

$$(1.6)$$
$$(1.7)$$
$$(1.8)$$

The precision of the apparatus is measured by the standard deviation, σ, of the infinite experiment:

$$\sigma^2 = \sigma^2(x) = \sum_i (x_i - X)^2 f(x_i) \tag{1.9}$$

$$= \sum_i [\tfrac{1}{2}(x_i + x_{i-1}) - X]^2 (x_i - x_{i-1}) f(x_i) \tag{1.10}$$

$$= \int_{-\infty}^{\infty} (x - X)^2 F(x)\, dx \tag{1.11}$$

$$= \overline{x^2} - (\bar{x})^2. \tag{1.12}$$

CHAPTER 2.   Interpretation of results

From n measurements the best estimate of the true value is the mean, X_n:

$$X_n = \bar{x} = \sum_i x_i / n. \tag{2.1}$$

The best estimate of the standard deviation is the adjusted r.m.s. deviation, s_n:

$$s_n^2 = n\sigma_n^2 / (n-1) = \sum_i (x_i - X_n)^2 / (n-1) \tag{2.2}$$

$$= n[\overline{x^2} - (\bar{x})^2] / (n-1). \tag{2.32}$$

The accuracy of X_n as an estimate of X is the standard error, $\sigma(x_n)$:

$$\sigma(X_n) = \sigma(x)/n^{\frac{1}{2}}. \tag{2.18}$$

The best estimate of the standard error is the adjusted error, S_n:

$$S_n = s_n / n^{\frac{1}{2}}. \tag{2.19}$$

The fractional error of S_n is

$$\sigma(S_n)/S_n \sim 1/(n-2)^{\frac{1}{2}}. \tag{2.22}$$

Writing the overall result as

$$X = X_n \pm S_n \tag{2.20}$$

means that there is approximately a $2:1$ probability that

$$X_n - S_n < X < X_n + S_n.$$

If

$$z = \alpha + ax + by + \ldots$$

then with n measurements of x, m of y, ..., the best estimate of the true value Z is $Z_{nm\ldots}$.

$$Z_{nm\ldots} = \alpha + aX_n + bY_m + \ldots. \tag{2.3}$$

The best estimate of precision, $\sigma(z)$, is $s_{nm\ldots}(z)$:

$$s_{nm}(z) = [a^2 s_n^2(x) + b^2 s_m^2(y) + \ldots]^{\frac{1}{2}}. \tag{2.5}$$

The best estimate of standard error, $\sigma(Z_{nm\ldots})$, is $S_{nm\ldots}(z)$:

$$S_{nm\ldots}(z) = [a^2 S_n^2(x) + b^2 S_m^2(y) + \ldots]^{\frac{1}{2}}. \tag{2.23}$$

If

$$z = \alpha x^a y^b \ldots,$$

the corresponding results are:

$$Z_{nm\ldots} = \alpha X_n^a Y_m^b \ldots, \tag{2.9}$$

$$s_{nm\ldots}(z)/Z_{nm\ldots} = [a^2 s_n^2(x)/X_n^2 + b^2 s_m^2(y)/Y_m^2 + \ldots]^{\frac{1}{2}}, \tag{2.11}$$

$$S_{nm\ldots}(z)/Z_{nm\ldots} = [a^2 S_n^2(x)/X_n^2 + b^2 S_m^2(y)/Y_m^2 + \ldots]^{\frac{1}{2}}. \tag{2.24}$$

If

$$z = f(x),$$

then

$$Z_n = f(X_n), \tag{2.13}$$

$$s_n(z) = f'(X_n) s_n(x), \tag{2.15}$$

$$S_n(z) = f'(X_n) S_n(x). \tag{2.25}$$

If

$$z = f(x, y, \ldots)$$

then

$$Z_{nm\ldots} = f(X_n, Y_m, \ldots), \tag{2.16}$$

$$s_{nm\ldots}(z) = [f_x^2 s_n^2(x) + f_y^2 s_m^2(y) + \ldots]^{\frac{1}{2}}, \tag{2.17}$$

$$S_{nm\ldots}(z) = [f_x^2 S_n^2(x) + f_y^2 S_m^2(y) + \ldots]^{\frac{1}{2}}, \tag{2.26}$$

If X_A is an assumed mean,

$$X_n = \sum_i (x_i - X_A)/n + X_A, \tag{2.28}$$

$$s_n^2 = \sum_i (x_i - X_A)^2/(n-1) - n(X_n - X_A)^2/(n-1). \tag{2.30}$$

CHAPTER 3. Least squares

The results of Chapter 2 are examples of the general principle of least squares. This states that the best interpretation of an experiment is that which minimizes the sum of the squared errors of individual measurements.

The best straight line,

$$y = ax + b,$$

linking n points (x_i, y_i), or line of regression of y on x, has for the best estimate of slope and intercept

$$a_n = [n\Sigma xy - \Sigma x\Sigma y]/[n\Sigma x^2 - (\Sigma x)^2], \tag{3.9}$$

$$b_m = [\Sigma x^2\Sigma y - \Sigma x\Sigma xy]/[n\Sigma x^2 - (\Sigma x)^2]. \tag{3.10}$$

The standard errors are

$$S_n(a) = n\sigma_n(y)/\{(n-2)[n\Sigma x^2 - (\Sigma x)^2]\}^{\frac{1}{2}}, \tag{3.11}$$

$$S_n(b) = n\sigma_n(y)(\Sigma x^2)^{\frac{1}{2}}/\{n(n-2)[n\Sigma x^2 - (\Sigma x)^2]\}^{\frac{1}{2}}. \tag{3.12}$$

The above expressions assume that only y values have errors:

$$n^2\sigma_n^2(y) = n\Sigma y^2 - (\Sigma y)^2 - [n\Sigma xy - \Sigma x\Sigma y]^2/[n\Sigma x^2 - (\Sigma x)^2]. \tag{3.13}$$

The correlation between y and x improves with $|r|$ as it varies from 0 to 1, where

$$r = \frac{n\Sigma xy - \Sigma x\Sigma y}{[n\Sigma x^2 - (\Sigma x)^2]^{\frac{1}{2}}[n\Sigma y^2 - (\Sigma y)^2]^{\frac{1}{2}}} \tag{3.27}$$

is the coefficient of correlation.

The correlation is likely to be significant when

$$|r| > 3/(n+7). \tag{3.26}$$

If x has the integer values $0, 1, \ldots, n-1$,

$$n\Sigma x^2 - (\Sigma x)^2 = n^2(n^2-1)/12. \tag{3.31}$$

Experimental values $X_n \pm S_n, X_m \pm S_m, \ldots$ of the same quantity combine as

$$X = X_{n,m,\ldots} \pm S_{n,m,\ldots},$$

where

$$X_{n,m,\ldots} = \frac{S_n^{-2}X_n + S_m^{-2}X_m + \ldots}{S_n^{-2} + S_m^{-2} + \ldots}, \tag{3.29}$$

$$S_{n,m,\ldots}^{-2} = S_n^{-2} + S_m^{-2} + \ldots . \tag{3.30}$$

Thus X_n is given the weight S_n^{-2}, X_m the weight S_m^{-2}, etc.

CHAPTER 4. Causes of error

Systematic errors arise from faults or changes in conditions which could be corrected or allowed for. Random errors are caused by intrinsic and unpredictable fluctuations in the apparatus.

A simple frequency distribution results from combining two independent random errors. It illustrates the basic laws of combining probabilities:

probability of [a followed by b] = probability of [a]

× probability of [b];

probability of [either a or b] = probability of [a]

+ probability of [b].

The various types of error should match each other in magnitude, and the number of figures recorded for each measurement should accord with this.

CHAPTER 5. Elementary theory of errors

The number of permutations of n distinguishable objects is

$$n! = n(n-1)\ldots \times 2 \times 1. \tag{5.1}$$

The number of combinations of n objects, taken r at a time, is

$$_nC_r = \frac{n!}{r!(n-r)!} = {_nC_{n-r}}. \tag{5.2}$$

n sources of error $\pm e$ give the binomial distribution or probability

$$Q(m;n) = \frac{n!}{2^n \left(\dfrac{n+m}{2}\right)! \left(\dfrac{n-m}{2}\right)!} \tag{5.3}$$

for an overall error $\varepsilon = me$. A limiting form of this ($n \to \infty$, $e \to 0$, $ne^2 \to \sigma^2$) is the Gaussian or normal distribution:

$$P(x; X, \sigma)\, dx = \frac{1}{(2\pi)^{\frac{1}{2}}\sigma} \exp\left[-\frac{(x-X)^2}{2\sigma^2}\right] dx, \qquad (5.4)$$

which is the probability of obtaining a measurement in $(x, x + dx)$.

This has true value X (mean, mode or median) and standard deviation σ. (5.11)

Probability of a measurement in $(X - \sigma, X + \sigma)$ is 0.683. (5.12)

For counting experiments the Poisson distribution,

$$P(r; \mu) = e^{-\mu}\mu^r/r!, \qquad (5.15)$$

is the probability of observing r counts.

This has a mean value μ and standard deviation $\mu^{\frac{1}{2}}$.
(5.19)
(5.20)

The Gaussian distribution is a fair approximation to the Poisson distribution for $\mu \geq 10$ and a very good one for $\mu \geq 30$.

CHAPTER 6. Likelihood, confidence and truth

If a distribution, $f(x)$, is proposed for measurements $x_1, x_2, \ldots, x_n$, the maximum likelihood determination of $f(x)$ is that which maximizes

$$P = f(x_1)f(x_2)\ldots f(x_n).$$

For a proposed Gaussian fit the maximum likelihood estimates are

$$X = \Sigma x_i/n, \qquad \sigma^2 = \Sigma(x_i - X)^2/n. \qquad \begin{matrix} (6.1) \\ (6.2) \end{matrix}$$

For a proposed Poisson fit to counts $r_1, r_2, \ldots, r_n$, the maximum likelihood estimate is

$$\mu = \Sigma r_i/n. \qquad (6.3)$$

X_n has a Gaussian distribution about X (central limit theorem). Then

$$X = X_n \pm S_n$$

indicates a confidence level of 68.3% for $(X_n - S_n, X_n + s_n)$ to contain X.

$$X = X_n \pm 2.58\, S_n$$

indicates a confidence level of 99.0%.

The maximum likelihood combination of $X_n \pm S_n$ and $X'_m \pm S'_m$ is $X \pm S_{n,m}$, where

$$X = \frac{S_n^2 S_m'^2}{S_n^2 + S_m'^2} \left(\frac{X_n}{S_n^2} + \frac{X'_m}{S_m'^2} \right) + \frac{S_n^2 S_m'^2 (S_n^2 - S_m'^2)}{(S_n^2 + S_m'^2)^4} (X_n - X'_m)^3, \quad (6.10)$$

$$S_{n,m}^{-2} = S_n^{-2} + S_m'^{-2} - \left(\frac{X_n - X'_m}{S_n^2 + S_m'^2} \right)^2 \left(\frac{1}{n} + \frac{1}{m} \right), \quad (6.11)$$

provided $(X_n - X'_m)^2 \ll \sigma_n^2, \sigma_m'^2$.

If $(X_n - X'_m)^2 \gg \sigma_n^2, \sigma_m'^2$ a first approximation is obtained by considering n measurements X_n and m measurements X'_m, but the consistency of the experiments is in doubt (Equations 6.12, 6.13, Problem 43).

The backing a measurement or set of measurements gives to a hypothesis is the probability of obtaining any set which would be worse according to the hypothesis.

If a hypothesis predicts that, on average, proportions $p_1, p_2, \ldots, p_m$ of measurements should fall in groups $1, 2, \ldots, m$, and, of n measurements made, $n_1, n_2, \ldots, n_m$ are actually found in these groups, then the backing is determined by

$$\chi^2 = \sum_{i=1}^{m} (n_i - np_i)^2/(np_i). \quad (6.19)$$

and the number of degrees of freedom. l constraints on the measurements ($l \geq 1$ in this case) reduce the degrees of freedom to

$$n' = m = l. \quad (6.21)$$

The backing for the hypothesis is then

$$P_{n'}(>\chi^2) = \frac{1}{2^{(n'-2)/2}[(n'-2)/2]!} \int_x^\infty \kappa^{n'-1} e^{-\kappa^2/2} \, d\kappa. \quad (6.18)$$

APPENDIX 1. The Gaussian or Normal Distribution Function

$$\phi(y) = (2\pi)^{-\frac{1}{2}} \exp(-y^2/2)$$

± y	0.00	0.02	0.04	0.06	0.08
0.0	0.3989	0.3989	0.3986	0.3982	0.3977
0.1	0.3970	0.3961	0.3951	0.3939	0.3925
0.2	0.3910	0.3894	0.3876	0.3857	0.3836
0.3	0.3814	0.3790	0.3765	0.3739	0.3712
0.4	0.3683	0.3653	0.3621	0.3589	0.3555
0.5	0.3521	0.3485	0.3448	0.3410	0.3372
0.6	0.3332	0.3292	0.3251	0.3209	0.3166
0.7	0.3123	0.3079	0.3034	0.2989	0.2943
0.8	0.2897	0.2850	0.2803	0.2756	0.2709
0.9	0.2661	0.2613	0.2565	0.2516	0.2468
1.0	0.2420	0.2371	0.2323	0.2275	0.2227
1.1	0.2179	0.2131	0.2083	0.2036	0.1989
1.2	0.1942	0.1895	0.1849	0.1804	0.1758
1.3	0.1714	0.1669	0.1626	0.1582	0.1539
1.4	0.1497	0.1456	0.1415	0.1374	0.1334
1.5	0.1295	0.1257	0.1219	0.1182	0.1145
1.6	0.1109	0.1074	0.1040	0.1006	0.0973
1.7	0.0940	0.0909	0.0878	0.0848	0.0818
1.8	0.0790	0.0761	0.0734	0.0707	0.0681
1.9	0.0656	0.0632	0.0608	0.0584	0.0562
2.0	0.0540	0.0519	0.0498	0.0478	0.0459
2.1	0.0440	0.0422	0.0404	0.0387	0.0371
2.2	0.0355	0.0339	0.0325	0.0310	0.0297
2.3	0.0283	0.0270	0.0258	0.0246	0.0235
2.4	0.0224	0.0213	0.0203	0.0194	0.0184
2.5	0.0175	0.0167	0.0158	0.0151	0.0143
2.6	0.0136	0.0129	0.0122	0.0116	0.0110
2.7	0.0104	0.0099	0.0093	0.0088	0.0084
2.8	0.0079	0.0075	0.0071	0.0067	0.0063
2.9	0.0060	0.0056	0.0053	0.0050	0.0047
3.0	0.0044	0.0042	0.0039	0.0037	0.0035

3.4609	0.001
4.0722	0.0001
4.6030	0.00001

APPENDIX 2. The Integral Gaussian Probability

$$\psi(y) = \left(\frac{2}{\pi}\right)^{\frac{1}{2}} \int_0^y e^{-y'^2/2} \, dy'$$

y	0.00	0.02	0.04	0.06	0.08
0.0	0.0000	0.0160	0.0319	0.0478	0.0638
0.1	0.0797	0.0955	0.1113	0.1271	0.1428
0.2	0.1585	0.1741	0.1897	0.2051	0.2205
0.3	0.2358	0.2510	0.2661	0.2812	0.2961
0.4	0.3108	0.3255	0.3401	0.3545	0.3688
0.5	0.3829	0.3969	0.4108	0.4245	0.4381
0.6	0.4515	0.4647	0.4778	0.4907	0.5035
0.7	0.5161	0.5285	0.5407	0.5527	0.5646
0.8	0.5763	0.5878	0.5991	0.6102	0.6211
0.9	0.6319	0.6424	0.6528	0.6629	0.6729
1.0	0.6827	0.6923	0.7017	0.7109	0.7199
1.1	0.7287	0.7373	0.7457	0.7540	0.7620
1.2	0.7699	0.7775	0.7850	0.7923	0.7995
1.3	0.8064	0.8132	0.8198	0.8262	0.8324
1.4	0.8385	0.8444	0.8501	0.8557	0.8611
1.5	0.8664	0.8715	0.8764	0.8812	0.8859
1.6	0.8904	0.8948	0.8990	0.9031	0.9070
1.7	0.9109	0.9146	0.9181	0.9216	0.9249
1.8	0.9281	0.9312	0.9342	0.9371	0.9399
1.9	0.9426	0.9451	0.9476	0.9500	0.9523
2.0	0.9545	0.9566	0.9586	0.9606	0.9625
2.1	0.9643	0.9660	0.9676	0.9692	0.9707
2.2	0.9722	0.9736	0.9749	0.9762	0.9774
2.3	0.9786	0.9797	0.9807	0.9817	0.9827
2.4	0.9836	0.9845	0.9853	0.9861	0.9869
2.5	0.9876	0.9883	0.9889	0.9895	0.9901
2.6	0.9907	0.9912	0.9917	0.9922	0.9926
2.7	0.9931	0.9935	0.9939	0.9942	0.9946
2.8	0.9949	0.9952	0.9955	0.9958	0.9960
2.9	0.9963	0.9965	0.9967	0.9969	0.9971
3.0	0.9973	0.9975	0.9976	0.9978	0.9979

3.2906	0.999
3.8901	0.9999
4.4172	0.99999

APPENDIX 3. The Poisson Distribution Function

$$P(r; \mu) = e^{-\mu}\mu^r/r!$$

r \ μ	0.2	0.4	0.6	0.8
0	0.8187	0.6703	0.5488	0.4493
1	0.1637	0.2681	0.3293	0.3595
2	0.0164	0.0536	0.0988	0.1438
3	0.0011	0.0072	0.0198	0.0383
4	0.0001	0.0007	0.0030	0.0077
5		0.0001	0.0004	0.0012
6				0.0002

Appendix 3 (continued)

r \ μ	1.0	2.0	3.0	4.0	5.0	6.0	7.0	8.0	9.0	10.0
0	0.3679	0.1353	0.0498	0.0183	0.0067	0.0025	0.0009	0.0003	0.0001	
1	0.3679	0.2707	0.1494	0.0733	0.0337	0.0149	0.0064	0.0027	0.0011	0.0005
2	0.1839	0.2707	0.2240	0.1465	0.0842	0.0446	0.0223	0.0107	0.0050	0.0023
3	0.0613	0.1804	0.2240	0.1954	0.1404	0.0892	0.0521	0.0286	0.0150	0.0076
4	0.0153	0.0902	0.1680	0.1954	0.1755	0.1339	0.0912	0.0573	0.0337	0.0189
5	0.0031	0.0361	0.1008	0.1563	0.1755	0.1606	0.1277	0.0916	0.0607	0.0378
6	0.0005	0.0120	0.0504	0.1042	0.1462	0.1606	0.1490	0.1221	0.0911	0.0631
7	0.0001	0.0034	0.0216	0.0595	0.1044	0.1377	0.1490	0.1396	0.1171	0.0901
8		0.0009	0.0081	0.0298	0.0653	0.1033	0.1304	0.1396	0.1318	0.1126
9		0.0002	0.0027	0.0132	0.0363	0.0688	0.1014	0.1241	0.1318	0.1251
10			0.0008	0.0053	0.0181	0.0413	0.0710	0.0993	0.1186	0.1251
11			0.0002	0.0019	0.0082	0.0225	0.0452	0.0722	0.0970	0.1137
12			0.0001	0.0006	0.0034	0.0113	0.0263	0.0481	0.0728	0.0948
13				0.0002	0.0013	0.0052	0.0142	0.0296	0.0504	0.0729
14				0.0001	0.0005	0.0022	0.0071	0.0169	0.0324	0.0521
15					0.0002	0.0009	0.0033	0.0090	0.0194	0.0347
16						0.0003	0.0014	0.0045	0.0109	0.0217
17						0.0001	0.0006	0.0021	0.0058	0.0128
18							0.0002	0.0009	0.0029	0.0071
19							0.0001	0.0004	0.0014	0.0037
20								0.0002	0.0006	0.0019
21								0.0001	0.0003	0.0009
22									0.0001	0.0004
23										0.0002
24										0.0001

Appendix 3 (continued)

r \ μ	12.0	14.0	16.0	18.0	20.0
0					
1	0.0001				
2	0.0004	0.0001			
3	0.0018	0.0004	0.0001		
4	0.0053	0.0013	0.0003	0.0001	
5	0.0127	0.0037	0.0010	0.0002	0.0001
6	0.0255	0.0087	0.0026	0.0007	0.0002
7	0.0427	0.0174	0.0060	0.0019	0.0005
8	0.0655	0.0304	0.0120	0.0042	0.0013
9	0.0874	0.0473	0.0213	0.0083	0.0029
10	0.1048	0.0663	0.0341	0.0150	0.0058
11	0.1144	0.0844	0.0496	0.0245	0.0106
12	0.1144	0.0984	0.0661	0.0368	0.0176
13	0.1056	0.1060	0.0814	0.0509	0.0271
14	0.0905	0.1060	0.0930	0.0655	0.0387
15	0.0724	0.0989	0.0992	0.0786	0.0516
16	0.0543	0.0866	0.0992	0.0884	0.0646
17	0.0383	0.0713	0.0934	0.0936	0.0760
18	0.0255	0.0554	0.0830	0.0936	0.0844
19	0.0161	0.0409	0.0699	0.0887	0.0888
20	0.0097	0.0286	0.0559	0.0798	0.0888
21	0.0055	0.0191	0.0426	0.0684	0.0846
22	0.0030	0.0121	0.0310	0.0560	0.0769
23	0.0016	0.0074	0.0216	0.0438	0.0669
24	0.0008	0.0043	0.0144	0.0328	0.0557
25	0.0004	0.0024	0.0092	0.0237	0.0446
26	0.0002	0.0013	0.0057	0.0164	0.0343
27	0.0001	0.0007	0.0034	0.0109	0.0254
28		0.0003	0.0019	0.0070	0.0181
29		0.0002	0.0011	0.0044	0.0125
30		0.0001	0.0006	0.0026	0.0083
31			0.0003	0.0015	0.0054
32			0.0001	0.0009	0.0034
33			0.0001	0.0005	0.0020
34				0.0002	0.0012
35				0.0001	0.0007
36				0.0001	0.0004
37					0.0002
38					0.0001
39					0.0001

APPENDIX 4. Hypothesis Test

$$P_{n'}(>\chi^2) = \left[2^{(n'-2)/2} \left(\frac{n'-2}{2} \right)! \right]^{-1} \int_{\chi}^{\infty} \kappa^{n'-1} e^{-\kappa^2/2} \, d\kappa$$

χ^2 \ n'	1.0	2.0	3.0	4.0	5.0
0.0	1.0000	1.0000	1.0000	1.0000	1.0000
1.0	0.3174	0.6065	0.8004	0.9098	0.9617
2.0	0.1575	0.3679	0.5726	0.7358	0.8493
3.0	0.0832	0.2231	0.3916	0.5578	0.7000
4.0	0.0455	0.1353	0.2615	0.4060	0.5494
5.0	0.0253	0.0821	0.1718	0.2873	0.4159
6.0	0.0143	0.0498	0.1116	0.1991	0.3062
7.0	0.0082	0.0302	0.0720	0.1359	0.2207
8.0	0.0048	0.0183	0.0462	0.0916	0.1564
9.0	0.0029	0.0111	0.0295	0.0611	0.1093
10.0	0.0018	0.0067	0.0188	0.0404	0.0755
11.0	0.0012	0.0041	0.0120	0.0266	0.0516
12.0	0.0008	0.0025	0.0076	0.0174	0.0350
13.0	0.0005	0.0015	0.0048	0.0113	0.0236
14.0	0.0004	0.0009	0.0031	0.0073	0.0158
15.0	0.0002	0.0006	0.0020	0.0047	0.0105
16.0	0.0002	0.0003	0.0013	0.0030	0.0070
17.0	0.0001	0.0002	0.0008	0.0019	0.0046
18.0	0.0001	0.0001	0.0005	0.0012	0.0030
19.0	0.0001	0.0001	0.0003	0.0008	0.0020
20.0	0.0001	0.0001	0.0002	0.0005	0.0013
21.0		0.0001	0.0001	0.0003	0.0009
22.0			0.0001	0.0002	0.0006
23.0			0.0001	0.0001	0.0004
24.0				0.0001	0.0002
25.0				0.0001	0.0002
26.0					0.0001
27.0					0.0001
28.0					
29.0					
30.0					

Appendix 4 (continued)

6.0	7.0	8.0	9.0	10.0	n' χ^2
1.0000	1.0000	1.0000	1.0000	1.0000	0.0
0.9856	0.9940	0.9982	0.9986	0.9998	1.0
0.9197	0.9600	0.9810	0.9917	0.9963	2.0
0.8088	0.8850	0.9344	0.9643	0.9814	3.0
0.6767	0.7798	0.8571	0.9114	0.9473	4.0
0.5438	0.6600	0.7576	0.8343	0.8912	5.0
0.4232	0.5398	0.6472	0.7399	0.8153	6.0
0.3208	0.4290	0.5366	0.6372	0.7254	7.0
0.2381	0.3327	0.4335	0.5343	0.6288	8.0
0.1736	0.2529	0.3423	0.4375	0.5321	9.0
0.1247	0.1888	0.2650	0.3507	0.4405	10.0
0.0884	0.1389	0.2017	0.2760	0.3575	11.0
0.0620	0.1008	0.1512	0.2135	0.2851	12.0
0.0430	0.0723	0.1118	0.1628	0.2237	13.0
0.0296	0.0514	0.0818	0.1225	0.1730	14.0
0.0203	0.0361	0.0591	0.0911	0.1321	15.0
0.0138	0.0252	0.0424	0.0670	0.0996	16.0
0.0093	0.0175	0.0301	0.0488	0.0744	17.0
0.0062	0.0120	0.0212	0.0352	0.0550	18.0
0.0042	0.0082	0.0149	0.0253	0.0403	19.0
0.0028	0.0056	0.0103	0.0180	0.0293	20.0
0.0018	0.0038	0.0071	0.0127	0.0211	21.0
0.0012	0.0026	0.0049	0.0089	0.0151	22.0
0.0008	0.0017	0.0034	0.0062	0.0107	23.0
0.0005	0.0012	0.0023	0.0043	0.0076	24.0
0.0003	0.0008	0.0016	0.0030	0.0053	25.0
0.0002	0.0005	0.0011	0.0021	0.0037	26.0
0.0001	0.0003	0.0007	0.0014	0.0026	27.0
0.0001	0.0002	0.0005	0.0010	0.0018	28.0
0.0001	0.0002	0.0003	0.0007	0.0012	29.0
	0.0001	0.0002	0.0004	0.0009	30.0

Appendix 4 (continued)

χ^2 \ n'	11.0	12.0	13.0	14.0	15.0
0.0	1.0000	1.0000	1.0000	1.0000	1.0000
2.0	0.9987	0.9994	0.9998	0.9999	1.0000
4.0	0.9699	0.9834	0.9912	0.9955	0.9977
6.0	0.8734	0.9161	0.9462	0.9665	0.9798
8.0	0.7135	0.7851	0.8437	0.8893	0.9239
10.0	0.5306	0.6160	0.6942	0.7622	0.8200
12.0	0.3639	0.4457	0.5279	0.6063	0.6793
14.0	0.2332	0.3007	0.3740	0.4497	0.5257
16.0	0.1412	0.1912	0.2492	0.3134	0.3822
18.0	0.0817	0.1157	0.1576	0.2068	0.2627
20.0	0.0454	0.0671	0.0953	0.1301	0.1720
22.0	0.0244	0.0375	0.0554	0.0786	0.1078
24.0	0.0128	0.0203	0.0312	0.0458	0.0651
26.0	0.0065	0.0107	0.0170	0.0259	0.0380
28.0	0.0032	0.0055	0.0091	0.0142	0.0216
30.0	0.0016	0.0028	0.0047	0.0076	0.0119
32.0	0.0008	0.0014	0.0024	0.0040	0.0064
34.0	0.0004	0.0007	0.0012	0.0021	0.0034
36.0	0.0002	0.0003	0.0006	0.0010	0.0018
38.0	0.0001	0.0002	0.0003	0.0005	0.0009
40.0		0.0001	0.0001	0.0003	0.0005
42.0			0.0001	0.0001	0.0002
44.0				0.0001	0.0001
46.0					0.0001
48.0					
50.0					

Appendix 4 (continued)

16.0	17.0	18.0	19.0	20.0	n' / χ^2
1.0000	1.0000	1.0000	1.0000	1.0000	0.0
1.0000	1.0000	1.0000	1.0000	1.0000	2.0
0.9989	0.9995	0.9998	0.9999	1.0000	4.0
0.9881	0.9932	0.9962	0.9979	0.9989	6.0
0.9489	0.9667	0.9786	0.9868	0.9919	8.0
0.8666	0.9038	0.9319	0.9532	0.9682	10.0
0.7440	0.8004	0.8472	0.8858	0.9161	12.0
0.5987	0.6673	0.7291	0.7839	0.8305	14.0
0.4530	0.5239	0.5925	0.6574	0.7166	16.0
0.3239	0.3889	0.4557	0.5225	0.5874	18.0
0.2202	0.2743	0.3328	0.3946	0.4579	20.0
0.1432	0.1848	0.2320	0.2843	0.3405	22.0
0.0895	0.1195	0.1550	0.1962	0.2424	24.0
0.0540	0.0745	0.0998	0.1302	0.1658	26.0
0.0316	0.0449	0.0621	0.0834	0.1094	28.0
0.0180	0.0264	0.0374	0.0518	0.0699	30.0
0.0100	0.0151	0.0220	0.0313	0.0433	32.0
0.0054	0.0084	0.0126	0.0184	0.0261	34.0
0.0029	0.0046	0.0071	0.0106	0.0154	36.0
0.0015	0.0025	0.0039	0.0059	0.0089	38.0
0.0008	0.0013	0.0021	0.0033	0.0050	40.0
0.0004	0.0007	0.0011	0.0018	0.0028	42.0
0.0002	0.0003	0.0006	0.0009	0.0015	44.0
0.0001	0.0002	0.0003	0.0005	0.0008	46.0
	0.0001	0.0002	0.0003	0.0004	48.0
		0.0001	0.0001	0.0002	50.0

Further reading

Fry, T. C. *Probability and Its Engineering Uses*, 2nd edition, Van Nostrand (1965).
Kendall, M. G. (and Stuart, A.). *The Advanced Theory of Statistics*, Griffin (1955, 1958).
Pugh, E. M., and Winslow, G. H. *The Analysis of Physical Measurements*. Addison-Wesley (1966).

Statistical Tables
Fisher, R. A., and Yates, F. *Statistical Tables for Biological, Agricultural and Medical Research*, 6th edition, Oliver and Boyd (1963).
Pearson, K. *Tables for Statisticians and Biometricians*, 3rd edition, Cambridge Univ. Press (1930).
Tables of Normal Probability Functions, National Bureau of Standards, Washington (1953).

Index

Page numbers in boldface type refer to chapter or section headings.

157